Math 6

A Reference Guide

Book Staff and Contributors

Carol McGehe   *Content Specialist*
Libby Riker   *Senior Text Editor*
Suzanne Montazer   *Creative Director, Print and ePublishing*
Stephanie Shaw Williams   *Senior Print Visual Designer, Cover Designer*
Jayoung Cho   *Senior Visual Designer*
Meredith Condit, Charlotte Fullerton   *Media Editors*
Susan Raley   *Senior Manager, Writers and Editors*
Luz Long, Abhilasha Parakh   *Senior Project Managers*

Paul Thomas   *Senior Director, Content and Assessment*
Kelly Engel   *Director, Mathematics Content Specialists*
Michelle Kitt   *Director, Instructional Design*
Jason Golomb   *Senior Director, Program Management Product Development*
Christopher Frescholtz   *Senior Director, Program Management*

Lisa Dimaio Iekel   *Director, Print Production and Manufacturing*

About K12 Inc.

K12 Inc. (NYSE: LRN) drives innovation and advances the quality of education by delivering state-of-the-art digital learning platforms and technology to students and school districts around the world. K12 is a company of educators offering its online and blended curriculum to charter schools, public school districts, private schools, and directly to families. More information can be found at K12.com.

ISBN: 978-1-60153-506-1 (online book)
ISBN: 978-1-60153-499-6 (printed book)

Printed by Walsworth, Marceline, MO, USA, August 2020

Contents

Number Properties

Fractions and Decimals

Rational Numbers

Expressions

Equations and Inequalities

Ratios, Rates, and Percents

Area, Surface Area, and Volume

Statistical Graphs

Measures of Center and Spread

Appendices

K¹² Summit Curriculum

And remember: The pages in your book are also online!

Go to the online course to look for these digital resources in your lessons:

 **– second MATH**

Videos will introduce you to each topic.

 **math CAST**

Visual learning with animations and interaction will help you master key skills.

 **Worked EXAMPLE**

Solve problems with the help of stepped examples.

 **APPLY it!**

Use real-world examples to practice what you've learned.

Number Properties

Cipher machines, such as this one from the 1940s, were used to write and read coded messages. Cryptography is the study of codes. Many codes, and attempts to break them, rely on number theory to work.

Division of Whole Numbers

You can divide to separate objects into equal groups or determine how many objects are in a given number of groups.

Dividing Whole Numbers

Definition

The result of dividing a dividend by a divisor is the **quotient**.

$$\begin{array}{r} 14 \\ 7\overline{)98} \end{array}$$

divisor → 7; 14 ← quotient; 98 ← dividend

How to Show Division

There are three ways to show division. In each case, the dividend is 100, the divisor is 4, and the quotient is 25.

With long division:

$$\begin{array}{r} 25 \\ 4\overline{)100} \end{array}$$

With a division symbol:

$$100 \div 4 = 25$$

With a fraction bar:

$$\frac{100}{4} = 25$$

EXAMPLE 1

Use long division to find the quotient.

$$12\overline{)1704}$$

SOLUTION

Use place value to divide. For example, 12 divides 1704 at least 100 times, so the 1 in the quotient is in the hundreds place. Multiply 100 times the divisor 12 to get 1200. Subtract and continue to divide.

$$
\begin{array}{r}
142 \\
12\,\overline{)1704} \\
-1200 \\
\hline
504 \\
-480 \\
\hline
24 \\
-24 \\
\hline
0
\end{array}
$$

▶ **Remember** Be careful to line up digits in a long-division problem.

CHECK

Use multiplication to check your answer by finding the product of the quotient and the divisor. The product should be the dividend.

Multiply. $12 \cdot 142 = 1704$ ✓ ▪

EXAMPLE 2

Write the quotient as a mixed number.

$$\frac{407}{100}$$

SOLUTION

There are 4 groups of 100 in 400, with 7 left over.

Write the 4 as the whole-number part of the quotient and the remainder over the divisor.

$$\frac{407}{100} = 4\frac{7}{100} \ \blacksquare$$

EXAMPLE 3

Use division to solve.

Steve spent $1128 for Internet service last year. His rate is the same each month. How much did he pay each month?

SOLUTION

The problem can be translated: $12\overline{)1128}$.

▶ **Think About It** Can 12 divide 1? No.
Can 12 divide 11? No.
Can 12 divide 112? Yes!

$$\begin{array}{r} 94 \\ 12\overline{)1128} \\ -108 \\ \hline 48 \\ -48 \\ \hline 0 \end{array}$$

The quotient is 94, so Steve paid $94 each month. ■

EXAMPLE 4

Use division to solve.

Petra must run 255 mi in 30 days to earn a medal. She plans to run the same distance each day. How far must she run each day?

SOLUTION

Divide 255 by 30.

$$\frac{255}{30} = ?$$

▶ **Think About It** Think of multiplication facts for 30.

$$30 \cdot 6 = 180$$
$$30 \cdot 7 = 210$$
$$30 \cdot 8 = 240$$
$$30 \cdot 9 = 270$$

The quotient is between 8 and 9, so the quotient is 8 plus a remainder.

$$\frac{255}{30} = 8\frac{15}{30} = 8\frac{1}{2}$$

Petra must run $8\frac{1}{2}$ mi each day. ■

Primes and Composites

All whole numbers greater than 1 are either prime or composite.

Identifying Prime and Composite Numbers

Definitions

A **prime number** is a whole number greater than 1 that has only two factors, 1 and itself.

A **composite number** is a whole number greater than 1 that is not prime. Composite numbers have more than two factors.

You can find the factors of a number to determine whether the number is prime or composite.

EXAMPLE

State whether the number is prime or composite.

A 24

SOLUTION
Find the factors of 24.

factors of 24: 1, 2, 3, 4, 6, 8, 12, 24

The number 24 has more than two factors. The number 24 is a composite number.

SOLUTION

factors of 17: 1, 17

The number 17 has only two factors, 1 and itself. The number 17 is a prime number. ▪

▶ **Think About It** Once you find more than two factors of a number, you know the number is composite since a prime number has only two factors.

Using Prime Factorization

The prime factorization of a number can be used to help solve many types of problems.

Prime Factorization

Definition

The **prime factorization** of a number is the multiplication equation showing the number as a product of its prime factors. The prime factors are typically written in ascending order in the equation.

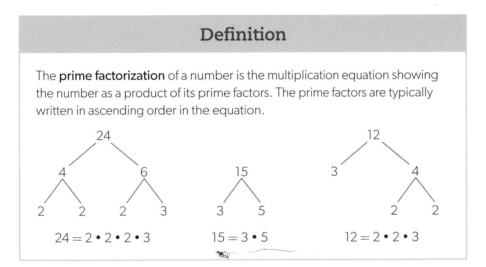

$24 = 2 \cdot 2 \cdot 2 \cdot 3$

$15 = 3 \cdot 5$

$12 = 2 \cdot 2 \cdot 3$

Finding the LCM and GCF

You can use prime factorization to find the least common multiple (LCM) and the greatest common factor (GCF) of two or more numbers.

EXAMPLE 1

Find the LCM of 12 and 20.

SOLUTION

Find the prime factorization for each number. Multiply each of the prime factors the greatest number of times they appear in any one prime factorization.

$$12 = 2 \bullet 2 \bullet 3 \qquad 20 = 2 \bullet 2 \bullet 5$$

The greatest number of times that 2 appears in either factorization is twice. The prime factors 3 and 5 each appear only once in either prime factorization.

$$2 \bullet 2 \bullet 3 \bullet 5 = 60$$

The LCM of 12 and 20 is 60. ■

EXAMPLE 2

Find the GCF of 36 and 24.

SOLUTION

Find the prime factorization for each number. Multiply each factor that has a match.

$$36 = 2 \bullet 2 \bullet 3 \bullet 3$$
$$24 = 2 \bullet 2 \bullet 2 \bullet 3$$

2 has two matches. 3 has one match.

$$2 \bullet 2 \bullet 3 = 12$$

The GCF of 36 and 24 is 12. ■

▶ **Remember** The LCM is the least multiple, other than 0, that is a common multiple of two or more numbers. The GCF is the greatest factor that is a common factor of two or more whole numbers.

The Distributive Property

When you simplify an expression involving parentheses, begin inside parentheses and work your way out.
There is another way to simplify expressions that have grouping symbols.

The distributive property combines multiplication with either addition or subtraction.

Distributive Property

For all numbers a, b, and c,

$$a(b+c) = ab + ac \text{ and } a(b-c) = ab - ac$$

Example

$$3(5+2) = 3 \cdot 5 + 3 \cdot 2$$
$$6(14-10) = 6 \cdot 14 - 6 \cdot 10$$

Verifying the Distributive Property

You can verify the distributive property by working inside the parenetheses first.

EXAMPLE 1

Verify the distributive property.

A $3(5+2) = 3 \bullet 5 + 3 \bullet 2$

> ▶ **Think About It** When you use the distributive property, you have *distributed* the factor through the terms inside the parentheses.

SOLUTION

On the left side, add inside parentheses first. On the right side, use the distributive property to multiply first.

$$3(5+2) = 3 \bullet 5 + 3 \bullet 2$$
$$3(7) = 15 + 6$$
$$21 = 21$$

B $6(14-10) = 6 \bullet 14 - 6 \bullet 10$

SOLUTION

On the left side, subtract inside parentheses first. On the right side, use the distributive property to multiply first.

$$6(14-10) = 6 \bullet 14 - 6 \bullet 10$$
$$6(4) = 84 - 60$$
$$24 = 24 \ \blacksquare$$

Using the Distributive Property to Rewrite Expressions

You can use the distributive property to change an addition expression without parentheses to one with parentheses (and vice versa).

EXAMPLE 2

Rewrite the expression without grouping symbols.

A $2(5+7)$

SOLUTION

$$2(5+7) = 2 \bullet 5 + 2 \bullet 7$$

B $3(4+5)$

SOLUTION

$$3(4+5) = 3 \bullet 4 + 3 \bullet 5 \ \blacksquare$$

EXAMPLE 3

Rewrite the expression with grouping symbols.

A $2 \cdot 3 + 2 \cdot 11$

SOLUTION
$$2 \cdot 3 + 2 \cdot 11 = 2(3 + 11)$$

B $8 \cdot 1 + 8 \cdot 7$

SOLUTION
$$8 \cdot 1 + 8 \cdot 7 = 8(1 + 7)$$

C $5r - 5 \cdot 12$

SOLUTION
$$5r - 5 \cdot 12 = 5(r - 12) \ \blacksquare$$

EXAMPLE 4

Rewrite the expression with grouping symbols.

A $36 + 60$

SOLUTION
$36 + 60 = 12(3 + 5)$

B $25 + 75$

SOLUTION
$25 + 75 = 25(1 + 3)$

C $72 + 45$

SOLUTION
$72 + 45 = 9(8 + 5) \ \blacksquare$

▶ Q&A

Q What is the greatest factor that 36 and 60 have in common?

A The greatest factor in common is 12, so write this factor outside the parentheses and divide 36 and 60 by 12. The quotients are written as a sum within the parentheses.

Using the Distributive Property to Evaluate Expressions

Using the distributive property to combine multiplication with either addition or subtraction gives you a powerful tool for evaluating certain types of expressions.

EXAMPLE 5

Use properties and mental math to evaluate the expression.

A $6 \cdot 74$

▶ **Think About It** When breaking a factor into a sum, look for numbers that are easier to multiply, such as 10 or 5.

SOLUTION

$$6 \cdot 74 = 6(70 + 4) \qquad \text{Write 74 as a sum.}$$
$$= 6 \cdot 70 + 6 \cdot 4 \qquad \text{Apply the distributive property.}$$
$$= 420 + 24 \qquad \text{Evaluate the expression.}$$
$$= 444$$

B $8 \cdot 99$

SOLUTION

$$8 \cdot 99 = 8(100 - 1) \qquad \text{Write 99 as a difference.}$$
$$= 8 \cdot 100 - 8 \cdot 1 \qquad \text{Apply the distributive property.}$$
$$= 800 - 8 \qquad \text{Evaluate the expression.}$$
$$= 792$$

▶ **Think About It** Use the methods shown in Example 5 to do mental math. In Example 5B, writing 99 as $100 - 1$ gives you numbers that are easy to multiply.

C $7 \cdot 67 + 7 \cdot 3$

SOLUTION

$$7 \cdot 67 + 7 \cdot 3 = 7(67 + 3) \qquad \text{Apply the distributive property.}$$

$$= 7(70) \qquad \text{The sum 70 is easier to multiply.}$$

$$= 490 \ \blacksquare$$

Solving Equations by Recognizing the Distributive Property

EXAMPLE 6

Solve the equation.

A $3 \cdot 5 + 3 \cdot a = 3(5 + 7)$

SOLUTION
By the distributive property, you know that $3 \cdot 5 + 3 \cdot \mathbf{7} = 3(5 + 7)$, so $a = 7$.

B $b(1.2 + 5.4) = 8 \cdot 1.2 + 8 \cdot 5.4$

SOLUTION
By the distributive property, you know that $\mathbf{8}(1.2 + 5.4) = 8 \cdot 1.2 + 8 \cdot 5.4$, so $b = 8$. $\blacksquare$

Application: Perimeter

EXAMPLE 7

Find the perimeter of the rectangle.

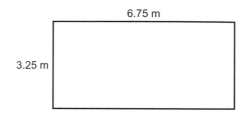

6.75 m

3.25 m

SOLUTION

$P = 2l + 2w$ Write the formula for perimeter of a rectangle.

$= 2 \cdot 6.75 + 2 \cdot 3.25$ Substitute 6.75 for length l and 3.25 for width w.

$= 2(6.75 + 3.25)$ Apply the distributive property and then add the decimals to get 10, which is easy to multiply.

$= 2(10)$

$= 20$

The perimeter is 20 m. ■

Properties of Whole Numbers

Properties can make simplifying expressions simpler.

Identifying Number Properties

Number Properties

Property	Example
Associative Properties The grouping of addends or factors doesn't change the sum or the product. $$a + (b+c) = (a+b) + c$$ $$a \bullet (b \bullet c) = (a \bullet b) \bullet c$$	$$2 + (3+4) = (2+3) + 4$$ $$5 \bullet (7 \bullet 9) = (5 \bullet 7) \bullet 9$$
Commutative Properties The order of addends or factors doesn't change the sum or the product. $$a + b = b + a$$ $$a \bullet b = b \bullet a$$	$$4 + 6 = 6 + 4$$ $$8 \bullet 9 = 9 \bullet 8$$
Distributive Properties For all numbers a, b, and c, $$a \bullet (b+c) = ab + ac$$ $$a \bullet (b-c) = ab - ac$$	$$3 \bullet (6+4) = 3 \bullet 6 + 3 \bullet 4$$ $$8 \bullet (5-2) = 8 \bullet 5 - 8 \bullet 2$$
Symmetric Property If $a = b$, then $b = a$.	If $(2+3) = 5$, then $5 = (2+3)$.
Transitive Property If $a = b$ and $b = c$, then $a = c$.	If $5 = x$ and $x = y$, then $5 = y$.

> **▶ Think About It** The commutative properties apply only to addition and multiplication.
>
> There are no commutative properties for subtraction or division.
>
> $$6 - 4 \neq 4 - 6$$
> $$12 \div 3 \neq 3 \div 12$$

EXAMPLE 1

Identify the property shown.

A $a + 3 = 3 + a$

SOLUTION

The order of the addends was changed.

$a + 3 = 3 + a$ shows the commutative property of addition.

B $2 \cdot (b + 7) = 2b + (2 \cdot 7)$

SOLUTION

The factor 2 is being distributed through the two addends in the parentheses.

$2 \cdot (b + 7) = 2b + (2 \cdot 7)$ shows the distributive property. ▪

Justifying Steps in Simplifying Expressions

If you can identify the properties being used to simplify an expression, you will be able to use them yourself to make simplifying expressions easier.

EXAMPLE 2

Justify each step in the solution.

$$5 \cdot (75 \cdot 2) = 5 \cdot (2 \cdot 75)$$
$$= (5 \cdot 2) \cdot 75$$
$$= 10 \cdot 75$$
$$= 750$$

SOLUTION

$5 \cdot (75 \cdot 2) = 5 \cdot (2 \cdot 75)$ Apply the commutative property of multiplication.

$= (5 \cdot 2) \cdot 75$ Apply the associative property of multiplication.

$= 10 \cdot 75$ Multiply.

$= 750$ Multiply. ■

Using Properties to Simplify Expressions

You can use the properties to rewrite expressions so that you can simplify them using mental math.

EXAMPLE 3

Use properties to simplify the expression.

A $6 \cdot 28$

SOLUTION

$6 \cdot 28 = 6 \cdot (20 + 8)$ Break 28 into the sum $20 + 8$.

$= 6 \cdot 20 + 6 \cdot 8$ Apply the distributive property.

$= 120 + 48$ Multiply.

$= 168$ Add.

$$6 \cdot 28 = 168$$

B $8 + (19 + 12)$

SOLUTION

$$8 + (19 + 12) = 8 + (12 + 19) \qquad \text{Apply the commutative property of addition.}$$
$$= (8 + 12) + 19 \qquad \text{Apply the associative property of addition.}$$
$$= 20 + 19 \qquad \text{Add.}$$
$$= 39 \qquad \text{Add.}$$

$$8 + (19 + 12) = 39 \ \blacksquare$$

▶ **Think About It** There are many different ways to use properties to simplify expressions. The ways shown in these problems are just examples.

Fractions and Decimals

Topic List

Many musical patterns can be described with fractions such as fifths or thirds. To understand music, it can help to understand the fractions that describe musical patterns.

Equivalent Fractions

A fraction is a number that represents a comparison of two values.

More than one fraction can name the same number.

Equivalent fractions, such as $\frac{1}{3}$ and $\frac{2}{6}$, are fractions with the same value.

$\frac{1}{3}$ [grid] $\frac{2}{6}$ [grid]

▶ **Remember** The numerator is the top number of a fraction. The denominator is the bottom number.

Writing Fractions in Simplest Form

A fraction is in simplest form when the numerator and denominator have no common factors other than 1. The fraction $\frac{2}{6}$ is not in simplest form because the numerator and denominator have a common factor of 2.

$$\frac{2}{6} = \frac{1 \cdot 2}{3 \cdot 2}$$

To write a fraction in simplest form, divide common factors from both the numerator and denominator until no common factors other than 1 remain. Dividing is the same as multiplying by the reciprocal. When you divide the numerator and denominator by the same value, it is the same as multiplying by a fraction with the same value in the numerator and denominator, which is the same as multiplying by a form of 1.

EXAMPLE 1

Write the fraction in simplest form.

$$\frac{24}{30}$$

SOLUTION

Divide the numerator and denominator by 6.

$$\frac{24}{30} = \frac{24 \div 6}{30 \div 6} = \frac{4}{5} \ \blacksquare$$

> ▶ **Think About It** If you use a common factor less than 6 in Example 1, you will have more than one step to complete.
>
> $$\frac{24 \div 2}{30 \div 2} = \frac{12}{15} \qquad \frac{12 \div 3}{15 \div 3} = \frac{4}{5}$$

Determining Whether Fractions Are Equivalent

EXAMPLE 2

Determine whether the fractions are equivalent fractions.

A $\frac{3}{18}$ and $\frac{6}{24}$

SOLUTION

Write each fraction in simplest form.

$$\frac{3}{18} = \frac{3 \div 3}{18 \div 3} \qquad\qquad \frac{6}{24} = \frac{6 \div 6}{24 \div 6}$$

$$= \frac{1}{6} \qquad\qquad\qquad\quad = \frac{1}{4}$$

The fractions are not equivalent fractions.

B $\dfrac{25}{45}$ and $\dfrac{10}{18}$

SOLUTION

Write each fraction in simplest form.

$$\dfrac{25}{45} = \dfrac{25 \div 5}{45 \div 5} \qquad\qquad\qquad \dfrac{10}{18} = \dfrac{10 \div 2}{18 \div 2}$$

$$= \dfrac{5}{9} \qquad\qquad\qquad\qquad\qquad = \dfrac{5}{9}$$

The fractions are equivalent fractions. ▪

Application: Entertainment

EXAMPLE 3

Use the chart to determine whether the same fraction of attendees at a movie each day were children.

Attendees	Sat.	Sun.
children	21	15
adults	35	25

SOLUTION

Write and compare fractions where the numerator is the number of children and the denominator is the total number of people.

$$\text{Saturday: } \dfrac{21}{21 + 35} = \dfrac{21}{56} = \dfrac{21 \div 7}{56 \div 7} = \dfrac{3}{8}$$

$$\text{Sunday: } \dfrac{15}{15 + 25} = \dfrac{15}{40} = \dfrac{15 \div 5}{40 \div 5} = \dfrac{3}{8}$$

The same fraction of attendees each day was children. ▪

Common Denominators

A common denominator enables you to compare, add, or subtract fractions.

Some multiples of 4 and 6 are shown. The common multiples are highlighted.

$$4 : 4, 8, \mathbf{12}, 16, 20, \mathbf{24}, 28, 32, \mathbf{36}, \ldots$$
$$6 : 6, \mathbf{12}, 18, \mathbf{24}, 30, \mathbf{36}, 42, \ldots$$

Definitions

The **least common multiple (LCM)** is the least number that is a common multiple of all numbers in a set. The **least common denominator (LCD)** is the least common multiple of two or more denominators.

The LCD of $\frac{3}{4}$ and $\frac{5}{6}$ is 12 because the LCM of 4 and 6 is 12.

▶ **Think About It** To find the LCM, you can also list multiples of the greater number until you find one that is a multiple of the other number.

Finding the Least Common Denominator

Find the LCD of the pair of fractions.

A $\frac{2}{5}$ and $\frac{3}{8}$

SOLUTION
Find the LCM of 5 and 8.

multiples of 5 : 5, 10, 15, 20, 25, 30, 35, **40**, . . .
multiples of 8 : 8, 16, 24, 32, **40**, . . .

The LCD is 40.

B $\frac{1}{8}$ and $\frac{5}{9}$

SOLUTION
Find the LCM of 6 and 9.

multiples of 6 : 6, 12, **18**, . . .
multiples of 9 : 9, **18**, 27, . . .

The LCD is 18. ■

▶ **Think About It** The product of the denominators is always a common multiple. This product may or may not be the least common multiple.

Expressing Fractions with the Same Denominator

Any fraction can be renamed to an equivalent fraction by multiplying both the numerator and denominator by the same number. When you multiply the numerator and denominator by the same number, you are multiplying the original fraction by a form of 1, resulting in an equivalent fraction.

▶ **Remember** Equivalent fractions are fractions with the same value.

EXAMPLE 2

Express the set of fractions using the same denominator.

A $\frac{3}{4}$ and $\frac{2}{3}$

SOLUTION

The LCD is 12. Rename both fractions with a denominator of 12.

$$\frac{3}{4} = \frac{3}{4} \cdot \frac{3}{3}$$

$$= \frac{3 \cdot 3}{4 \cdot 3}$$

$$= \frac{9}{12}$$

$$\frac{2}{3} = \frac{2}{3} \cdot \frac{4}{4}$$

$$= \frac{2 \cdot 4}{3 \cdot 4}$$

$$= \frac{8}{12}$$

The fractions are $\frac{9}{12}$ and $\frac{8}{12}$.

▶ **Think About It** In Example 2, you are using the LCD. Other fractions are possible, such as $\frac{18}{24}$ and $\frac{16}{24}$ for Example 2A.

B $\frac{11}{18}$, $\frac{1}{54}$, and $\frac{2}{27}$

SOLUTION

The LCD is 54. Rename $\frac{11}{18}$ and $\frac{2}{27}$.

$$\frac{11}{18} = \frac{11}{18} \cdot \frac{3}{3}$$

$$= \frac{11 \cdot 3}{18 \cdot 3}$$

$$= \frac{33}{54}$$

$$\frac{2}{27} = \frac{2}{27} \cdot \frac{2}{2}$$

$$= \frac{2 \cdot 2}{27 \cdot 2}$$

$$= \frac{4}{54}$$

The fractions are $\frac{33}{54}$, $\frac{1}{54}$, and $\frac{4}{54}$. ■

Comparing Fractions

When fractions have a common denominator, you can compare them by comparing the numerators. For example, $\frac{4}{7} > \frac{3}{7}$ because $4 > 3$. When the fractions have unlike denominators, rename one or both fractions so that they have a common denominator. Then compare the numerators.

EXAMPLE 3

Compare the fractions using $>$, $<$, or $=$.

A $\frac{7}{10}$ and $\frac{2}{5}$

SOLUTION

Rename $\frac{2}{5}$ with a denominator of 10.

$\frac{2}{5} = \frac{2 \cdot 2}{5 \cdot 2}$ Multiply the numerator and denominator by 2.

$\quad = \frac{4}{10}$

Compare $\frac{7}{10}$ and $\frac{4}{10}$. Because $7 > 4$, $\frac{7}{10} > \frac{4}{10}$, and $\frac{7}{10} > \frac{2}{5}$.

B $\frac{2}{3}$ and $\frac{3}{4}$

SOLUTION

Rename both fractions with a denominator of 12.

$\frac{2}{3} = \frac{2 \cdot 4}{3 \cdot 4}$ $\qquad\qquad\qquad$ $\frac{3}{4} = \frac{3 \cdot 3}{4 \cdot 3}$

$\quad = \frac{8}{12}$ $\qquad\qquad\qquad\qquad$ $\quad = \frac{9}{12}$

Compare $\frac{8}{12}$ and $\frac{9}{12}$. Because $8 < 9$, $\frac{8}{12} < \frac{9}{12}$, and $\frac{2}{3} < \frac{3}{4}$.

C $\frac{80}{100}$ and $\frac{4}{5}$

SOLUTION

Rename $\frac{4}{5}$ with a denominator of 100.

$$\frac{4}{5} = \frac{4 \cdot 20}{5 \cdot 20}$$

$$= \frac{80}{100}$$

Because $\frac{80}{100} = \frac{80}{100}$, $\frac{80}{100} = \frac{4}{5}$. ∎

> ▶ **Think About It** Any common denominator, not necessarily the LCD, can be used to compare fractions.

Application: Competition

EXAMPLE 4

A Jordan ran $\frac{7}{8}$ mi and Miguel ran $\frac{4}{5}$ mi. Who ran farther?

SOLUTION

Compare $\frac{7}{8}$ and $\frac{4}{5}$ using the LCD of 40.

Jordan: $\frac{7}{8} = \frac{7 \cdot 5}{8 \cdot 5}$ $\qquad\qquad$ Miguel: $\frac{4}{5} = \frac{4 \cdot 8}{5 \cdot 8}$

$\qquad\quad = \frac{35}{40}$ $\qquad\qquad\qquad\qquad\quad = \frac{32}{40}$

Jordan ran farther, because $\frac{35}{40}$ mi is a longer distance than $\frac{32}{40}$ mi.

B Three neighbors had a tomato-growing contest. The weights of their best tomatoes are shown in the table. List the weights from greatest to least.

Contestant	Margo	Julie	Hank
Tomato weight (lb)	$\dfrac{11}{16}$	$\dfrac{1}{2}$	$\dfrac{3}{4}$

SOLUTION

Compare the fractions using the LCD of 16.

Margo: $\dfrac{11}{16}$

Julie: $\dfrac{1}{2} = \dfrac{1 \cdot 8}{2 \cdot 8}$

$= \dfrac{8}{16}$

Hank: $\dfrac{3}{4} = \dfrac{3 \cdot 4}{4 \cdot 4}$

$= \dfrac{12}{16}$

The weights from greatest to least are $\dfrac{3}{4}$ lb, $\dfrac{11}{16}$ lb, and $\dfrac{1}{2}$ lb. ■

Adding and Subtracting Fractions

To add and subtract fractions, start by expressing each fraction with the same denominator. Some answers will need to be simplified by expressing the fraction in simplest form. Other answers may need to be simplified by writing an improper fraction as a mixed number.

Improper Fractions and Mixed Numbers

A fraction can represent a number greater than one.

These figures illustrate $\frac{3}{2}$.

Each shaded area is one-half. There are three one-halves shaded.

Another way to write the number illustrated by the figures is $1\frac{1}{2}$ because there is one whole and one half rectangle shaded.

Definitions
An **improper fraction** is a fraction in which the numerator is greater than or equal to the denominator.
A **mixed number** is a number consisting of both a whole number and a fraction.

How to Convert Improper Fractions to Mixed Numbers

Step 1 Divide the numerator by the denominator.

Step 2 Use the quotient as the whole number and the remainder as the numerator.

Step 3 Keep the original denominator.

EXAMPLE 1

Convert the improper fraction to a mixed number.

$$\frac{23}{8}$$

SOLUTION

$$8\overline{)23}^{\,2\,r7}$$ Divide the numerator by the denominator.

$$2\frac{7}{8}$$ Use the quotient as the whole number and the remainder as the numerator. ▪

▶ **Think About It** Be careful when using a calculator. Most calculators will give the quotient as a decimal.

$$23 \div 8 = 2.875$$
$$45 \div 6 = 7.5$$

Adding and Subtracting Fractions

Like Fractions (same denominator)

- Add or subtract the numerators.

- Keep the same denominator.

- Simplify if possible.

Unlike Fractions (different denominators)

- Write equivalent fractions as needed so that the fractions have the same denominator.

- Then add or subtract the like fractions.

Adding and Subtracting Like Fractions

EXAMPLE 2

Find the sum or difference. Write the answer in simplest form.

$$\frac{2}{7} + \frac{4}{7}$$

SOLUTION

$\frac{2}{7} + \frac{4}{7} = \frac{2+4}{7}$ Add the numerators. Keep the same denominator.

$= \frac{6}{7}$ Simplify. The fraction is already in simplest form. ∎

Adding and Subtracting Unlike Fractions

EXAMPLE 3

Find the sum. Write the answer in simplest form.

A $\dfrac{2}{8} + \dfrac{5}{12}$

SOLUTION
The LCD of 8 and 12 is 24.

$$\dfrac{2}{8} + \dfrac{5}{12} = \dfrac{6}{24} + \dfrac{10}{24} \qquad \text{Multiply 2 and 8 each by 3 to get } \dfrac{6}{24}. \text{ Multiply 5 and 12 each by 2 to get } \dfrac{10}{24}.$$

$$= \dfrac{16}{24} \qquad \text{Add the numerators.}$$

$$= \dfrac{2}{3} \qquad \text{Simplify.}$$

> ▶ **Think About It** To find the LCD, multiply the greater denominator by 1, 2, 3, 4, and so on. Stop when you find a multiple that the other denominator divides evenly.

B $\dfrac{4}{6} + \dfrac{8}{9}$

SOLUTION
The LCD of 6 and 9 is 18.

$$\dfrac{4}{6} + \dfrac{8}{9} = \dfrac{12}{18} + \dfrac{16}{18} \qquad \text{Multiply 4 and 6 each by 3 to get } \dfrac{12}{18}. \text{ Multiply 8 and 9 each by 2 to get } \dfrac{16}{18}.$$

$$= \dfrac{28}{18} \qquad \text{Add the numerators.}$$

$$= \dfrac{14}{9} \qquad \text{Simplify.}$$

$$= 1\dfrac{5}{9} \qquad \text{Write the improper fraction as a mixed number.} \ \blacksquare$$

EXAMPLE 4

Find the difference. Write the answer in simplest form.

$$\frac{4}{5} - \frac{2}{15}$$

SOLUTION

The LCD of 5 and 15 is 15.

$\frac{4}{5} - \frac{2}{15} = \frac{12}{15} - \frac{2}{15}$ Rewrite $\frac{4}{5}$ as $\frac{12}{15}$. Note that $\frac{2}{15}$ already has a denominator of 15.

$\phantom{\frac{4}{5} - \frac{2}{15}} = \frac{10}{15}$ Subtract the numerators.

$\phantom{\frac{4}{5} - \frac{2}{15}} = \frac{2}{3}$ Simplify. ▪

EXAMPLE 5

A bag of red grapes weighs $\frac{1}{2}$ lb. A bag of green grapes weighs $\frac{9}{10}$ lb. How much more does the bag of green grapes weigh than the bag of red grapes?

SOLUTION

Find $\frac{9}{10} - \frac{1}{2}$.

$\frac{9}{10} - \frac{1}{2} = \frac{9}{10} - \frac{5}{10}$ The LCD is 10. Rewrite $\frac{1}{2}$.

$\phantom{\frac{9}{10} - \frac{1}{2}} = \frac{4}{10}$ Subtract the numerators.

$\phantom{\frac{9}{10} - \frac{1}{2}} = \frac{2}{5}$ Simplify.

The bag of green grapes weighs $\frac{2}{5}$ lb more than the bag of red grapes weighs. ▪

Adding and Subtracting Mixed Numbers

EXAMPLE 6

Find the sum. Write the sum in simplest form.

$$2\frac{1}{6} + 5\frac{1}{10}$$

SOLUTION

The LCD of 6 and 10 is 30.

$$2\frac{1}{6} + 5\frac{1}{10} = 2\frac{5}{30} + 5\frac{3}{30}$$ Renwrite each mixed number with a denominator of 30.

$$= 7\frac{8}{30}$$ Add whole numbers and fractions.

$$= 7\frac{4}{15}$$ Simplify. ■

> ▶ **Think About It** When working with mixed numbers, use estimation to check your answer. Round each mixed number to the nearest whole number and then add or subtract.

EXAMPLE 7

Find the difference. Write the difference in simplest form.

$$9\frac{3}{4} - 1\frac{5}{12}$$

SOLUTION

The LCD of 4 and 12 is 12.

$$9\frac{3}{4} - 1\frac{5}{12} = 9\frac{9}{12} - 1\frac{5}{12}$$ Rewrite the first denominator with a denominator of 12.

$$= 8\frac{4}{12}$$ Subtract the whole numbers and fractions.

$$= 8\frac{1}{3}$$ Simplify. ■

EXAMPLE 8

Henry bought $6\frac{1}{2}$ lb of shrimp. He cooked $1\frac{7}{8}$ lb yesterday. How much shrimp does he have left to cook?

SOLUTION

Find $6\frac{1}{2} - 1\frac{7}{8}$.

$6\frac{1}{2} - 1\frac{7}{8} = 6\frac{4}{8} - 1\frac{7}{8}$ Use a common denominator of 8. Rewrite $6\frac{1}{2}$.

$6\frac{1}{2} - 1\frac{7}{8} = 6\frac{4}{8} - 1\frac{7}{8}$ Notice that regrouping is necessary to subtract the fractions.

$\qquad\qquad = 5 + 1\frac{4}{8} - 1\frac{7}{8}$ Think of 6 wholes as $5 + 1$.

$\qquad\qquad = 5 + \frac{8}{8} + \frac{4}{8} - 1\frac{7}{8}$ Rename 1 as $\frac{8}{8}$ and add to $\frac{4}{8}$.

$\qquad\qquad = 5\frac{12}{8} - 1\frac{7}{8}$ Regroup.

$\qquad\qquad = 4\frac{5}{8}$ Subtract whole numbers and fractions.

Henry has $4\frac{5}{8}$ lb of shrimp left to cook. ▪

> ► **Q&A**
>
> **Q** Is there another way to find the difference?
>
> **A** Instead of renaming $6\frac{4}{8}$ as $5\frac{12}{8}$, you could write $6\frac{1}{2}$ and $1\frac{7}{8}$ as improper fractions and then subtract. This method can lead to more errors, so be careful if you choose this approach.

Multiplying Fractions

You can use a diagram to understand multiplication of fractions.

This figure illustrates $\frac{1}{3}$ of a whole.

One-half of the shaded section is $\frac{1}{2}$ of $\frac{1}{3}$, or $\frac{1}{2} \cdot \frac{1}{3}$.

This figure shows $\frac{1}{6}$ of the whole.

Multiplying Fractions

The example suggests that when you multiply two fractions, you can multiply the numerators and the denominators. In fact, that's true.

Multiplying Fractions	
Property	**Example**
$\dfrac{a}{b} \cdot \dfrac{c}{d} = \dfrac{ac}{bd}$ $b \neq 0, d \neq 0$	$\dfrac{2}{3} \cdot \dfrac{5}{7} = \dfrac{2 \cdot 5}{3 \cdot 7} = \dfrac{10}{21}$

It is customary to write the product of fractions in simplest form.

EXAMPLE 1

Find the product and simplify.

$$\frac{1}{2} \cdot \frac{4}{5}$$

SOLUTION

$\frac{1}{2} \cdot \frac{4}{5} = \frac{1 \cdot 4}{2 \cdot 5}$ Multiply the numerators and the denominators.

$\qquad = \frac{4}{10}$

$\qquad = \frac{2}{5}$ Write the fraction in simplest form. ▪

Multiplying by Simplifying First

Common factors in either numerator can be divided out with common factors in either denominator. You can combine the fractions, then simplify; or you can simplify before combining the fractions. It is common practice to simplify first.

EXAMPLE 2

Divide out common factors. Then multiply.

$$\frac{3}{8} \cdot \frac{4}{5}$$

SOLUTION

$\frac{3}{8} \cdot \frac{4}{5} = \frac{3}{\overset{}{\underset{2}{8}}} \cdot \frac{\overset{1}{4}}{5}$ Divide out the common factor of 4 and show the new factors.

$\qquad = \frac{3 \cdot 1}{2 \cdot 5}$ Multiply 3 • 1 and 2 • 5.

$\qquad = \frac{3}{10}$ ▪

▶ **Think About It** To avoid errors, be sure to write the factors that remain after the common factors are divided out.

EXAMPLE 3

Write the mixed number as an improper fraction and then multiply.

$$3\frac{1}{2} \cdot \frac{6}{7}$$

SOLUTION

$$3\frac{1}{2} \cdot \frac{6}{7} = \frac{7}{2} \cdot \frac{6}{7}$$ Rewrite the mixed number as an improper fraction.

$$= \frac{\overset{1}{\cancel{7}}}{\underset{1}{\cancel{2}}} \cdot \frac{\overset{3}{\cancel{6}}}{\underset{1}{\cancel{7}}}$$ Divide 7 and 7 by 7. Divide 6 and 2 by 2. Show the new factors.

$$= \frac{1}{1} \cdot \frac{3}{1}$$ Multiply numerators. Multiply denominators.

$$= \frac{3}{1}$$ Simplify.

$$= 3 \ \blacksquare$$

EXAMPLE 4

Write both mixed numbers as improper fractions and then multiply.

$$2\frac{2}{5} \cdot 2\frac{3}{16}$$

SOLUTION

$$2\frac{2}{5} \cdot 2\frac{3}{16} = \frac{12}{5} \cdot \frac{35}{16}$$ Rewrite the mixed numbers as improper fractions.

$$= \frac{\overset{3}{\cancel{12}}}{\underset{1}{\cancel{5}}} \cdot \frac{\overset{7}{\cancel{35}}}{\underset{4}{\cancel{16}}}$$ Divide 12 and 16 by 4. Divide 5 and 35 by 5.

$$= \frac{3}{1} \cdot \frac{7}{4}$$ Multiply numerators. Multiply denominators.

$$= \frac{21}{4}$$ Simplify.

$$= 5\frac{1}{4} \ \blacksquare$$

EXAMPLE 5

Tino has $\frac{3}{4}$ gal of juice. He drinks $\frac{1}{3}$ of the juice. How many gallons of juice does he drink?

SOLUTION

Find $\frac{1}{3}$ of $\frac{3}{4}$, or $\frac{1}{3} \cdot \frac{3}{4}$.

$\frac{1}{3} \cdot \frac{3}{4} = \frac{1}{1} \cdot \frac{1}{4} = \frac{1}{4}$ Simplify first and then multiply.

Tino drinks $\frac{1}{4}$ gal juice. ▪

EXAMPLE 6

Raoul is $6\frac{2}{3}$ ft tall. His sister is $\frac{3}{4}$ as tall as Raoul. How tall is Raoul's sister?

SOLUTION

Find $\frac{3}{4}$ of $6\frac{2}{3}$, or $\frac{3}{4} \cdot 6\frac{2}{3}$.

Rewrite mixed numbers as improper fractions. Simplify, if possible, and then multiply.

$$\frac{3}{4} \cdot 6\frac{2}{3} = \frac{3}{4} \cdot \frac{20}{3}$$
$$= \frac{1}{1} \cdot \frac{5}{1}$$
$$= 5$$

Raoul's sister is 5 ft tall. ▪

EXAMPLE 7

A bag of Gabby's Granola contains $1\frac{1}{8}$ lb granola. Michele pours $3\frac{1}{3}$ bags of granola into a large bowl. How much granola is in the bowl?

SOLUTION

Find $3\frac{1}{3}$ groups of $1\frac{1}{8}$, or $3\frac{1}{3} \cdot 1\frac{1}{8}$.

Rewrite mixed numbers as improper fractions. Simplify, if possible, and then multiply.

$$3\frac{1}{3} \cdot 1\frac{1}{8} = \frac{10}{3} \cdot \frac{9}{8}$$

$$= \frac{5}{1} \cdot \frac{3}{4}$$

$$= \frac{15}{4}$$

$$\frac{15}{4} = 3\frac{3}{4} \qquad \text{Rewrite as a mixed number.}$$

There are $3\frac{3}{4}$ lb of granola in the bowl. ■

Application: Cooking

EXAMPLE 8

Keisha wants to bake 24 soft pretzels, but the recipe she has makes 48 soft pretzels.

A What fraction of each ingredient should she use?

SOLUTION

$$\frac{\text{soft pretzels wanted}}{\text{total recipe makes}} = \frac{24}{48} = \frac{1}{2}$$

Keisha should use $\frac{1}{2}$ of the amount of each ingredient in the original recipe.

B The recipe calls for $\frac{3}{4}$ cup of flour. How much flour should Keisha use?

SOLUTION

Find $\frac{1}{2}$ of $\frac{3}{4}$.

▶ **Remember** The word *of* indicates multiplication.

$$\frac{1}{2} \cdot \frac{3}{4} = \frac{3}{8}$$

Keisha should use $\frac{3}{8}$ cup of flour. ▪

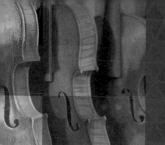

Dividing Fractions

Division separates a number into equal groups or determines the number of equal groups for a given number of objects.

Sometimes the divisor and dividend are fractions.

This figure illustrates $\frac{2}{3}$ of a whole.

This figure shows $\frac{1}{6}$ of the whole.

There are four $\frac{1}{6}$ in $\frac{2}{3}$. That is, $\frac{2}{3} \div \frac{1}{6} = 4$.

Finding Reciprocals of Fractions

The reciprocal of a number is used when dividing fractions.

▶ **Remember** The reciprocal is also called the multiplicative inverse.

Reciprocal of a Fraction

For any nonzero a and b,

$$\frac{a}{b} = \frac{b}{a}$$

Example

$$\frac{2}{3} = \frac{3}{2}$$

EXAMPLE 1

Find the reciprocal of the number.

A $\dfrac{9}{10}$

B $\dfrac{1}{5}$

SOLUTION
The reciprocal is $\dfrac{10}{9}$.

SOLUTION
The reciprocal is $\dfrac{5}{1}$, or 5. ■

▶ **Think About It** To find a reciprocal, "flip" the fraction. Check your answer by multiplying.

$$\dfrac{9}{10} \cdot \dfrac{10}{9} = \dfrac{90}{90} = 1$$

To divide fractions, multiply the divisor by the **reciprocal** of the dividend.

▶ **Remember** In $x \div y$, x is the dividend and y is the divisor.

Dividing Fractions

Property	Example
$\dfrac{a}{b} \div \dfrac{c}{d} = \dfrac{a}{b} \cdot \dfrac{d}{c} = \dfrac{ad}{bc}$ $b \neq 0, c \neq 0, d \neq 0$	$\dfrac{2}{3} \div \dfrac{1}{6} = \dfrac{2}{3} \cdot \dfrac{6}{1} = \dfrac{12}{3} = 4$

Dividing Fractions

EXAMPLE 2

Find the quotient and simplify.

A $\frac{1}{2} \div \frac{4}{6}$

SOLUTION

$\frac{1}{2} \div \frac{4}{6} = \frac{1}{2} \cdot \frac{6}{4}$ Multiply by the reciprocal.

$= \frac{1 \cdot 6}{2 \cdot 4}$ Multiply the numerators and the denominators.

$= \frac{6}{8}$

$= \frac{3}{4}$ Write in simplest form.

B $\frac{2}{3} \div 6$

SOLUTION

$\frac{2}{3} \div 6 = \frac{2}{3} \cdot \frac{1}{6}$ Multiply by the reciprocal.

$= \frac{2 \cdot 1}{3 \cdot 6}$ Multiply the numerators and the denominators.

$= \frac{2}{18}$

$= \frac{1}{9}$ Write in simplest form.

C $\frac{5}{8} \div 2\frac{1}{2}$

SOLUTION

$\frac{5}{8} \div 2\frac{1}{2} = \frac{5}{8} \div \frac{5}{2}$ Rewrite the mixed number as an improper fraction.

$= \frac{5}{8} \cdot \frac{2}{5}$ Multiply by the reciprocal.

$= \frac{\overset{1}{\cancel{5}}}{\underset{4}{\cancel{8}}} \cdot \frac{\overset{1}{\cancel{2}}}{\underset{1}{\cancel{5}}}$ Divide out common factors.

$= \frac{1}{4}$ Multiply.

D $8\frac{2}{3} \div 4\frac{2}{5}$

SOLUTION

$8\frac{2}{3} \div 4\frac{2}{5} = \frac{26}{3} \div \frac{22}{5}$ Rewrite the mixed numbers as improper fractions.

$\frac{26}{3} \cdot \frac{5}{22} = \frac{\overset{13}{\cancel{26}}}{3} \cdot \frac{5}{\underset{11}{\cancel{22}}}$ Multiply by the reciprocal. Divide out common factors.

$= \frac{65}{33}$ Multiply.

$= 1\frac{32}{33}$ Rewrite the improper fraction as a mixed number.

▶ **Think About It** Use estimation to check your answer. Round each mixed number to a whole number. Since 9 ÷ 5 is about 2, the answer seems reasonable.

E The area of a rectangle is $\frac{7}{12}$ m^2. The length is $\frac{3}{4}$ m. What is the width of the rectangle?

SOLUTION

$\frac{7}{12} \div \frac{3}{4} = \frac{7}{12} \cdot \frac{4}{3}$ Use division to solve. Multiply by the reciprocal.

$= \frac{7}{\underset{3}{\cancel{12}}} \cdot \frac{\overset{1}{\cancel{4}}}{3}$ Divide out common factors.

$= \frac{7}{9}$ Multiply.

The width of the rectangle is $\frac{7}{9}$ m.

F Mary has $5\frac{1}{2}$ cups of muffin mix. She uses $\frac{1}{4}$ cup of mix for each muffin.

How many muffins can she make?

SOLUTION

$5\frac{1}{2} \div \frac{1}{4} = \frac{11}{2} \div \frac{1}{4}$ Use division to solve. Rewrite the mixed number as an improper fraction.

$\dfrac{11}{\overset{}{\underset{1}{2}}} \cdot \dfrac{\overset{2}{4}}{1} = \dfrac{11}{1} \cdot \dfrac{2}{1}$ Multiply by the reciprocal. Divide out common factors.

$\dfrac{22}{1} = 22$ Multiply.

Mary can make 22 muffins.

> ▶ **Remember** When simplifying a fraction that has 1 as the denominator, write the numerator as a whole number, without the denominator.

G Jake buys $4\frac{1}{8}$ ft of string. He uses $1\frac{1}{4}$ ft of string to make a keychain.

How many whole keychains can he make?

SOLUTION

$4\frac{1}{8} \div 1\frac{1}{4} = \frac{33}{8} \div \frac{5}{4}$ Use division to solve. Rewrite the mixed numbers as improper fractions.

$\dfrac{33}{\overset{}{\underset{2}{8}}} \cdot \dfrac{\overset{1}{4}}{5} = \dfrac{33}{2} \cdot \dfrac{1}{5}$ Multiply by the reciprocal. Divide out common factors.

$\dfrac{33}{10} = 3\dfrac{3}{10}$ Multiply. Write the improper fraction as a mixed number.

Since $3\frac{3}{10}$ is between 3 and 4, Jake can make between 3 and 4 keychains.

He does not have enough string for 4, so he can make 3 keychains. ◼

> ▶ **Think About It** Sometimes you need to round to a whole number so that the answer makes sense.

Application: Sewing

EXAMPLE 3

Three-fourths yard of fabric is divided into 6 sections, each with equal length.
How long is each section?

SOLUTION

Divide: $\dfrac{3}{4} \div 6 = \dfrac{\overset{1}{\cancel{3}}}{4} \cdot \dfrac{1}{\underset{2}{\cancel{6}}}$ Multiply by the reciprocal. Divide out the common factor of 3.

$\qquad\qquad = \dfrac{1}{8}$ Multiply.

Each section is $\dfrac{1}{8}$ yd long.

CHECK

If each section is $\dfrac{1}{8}$ yd long, then the total length should be $6 \cdot \dfrac{1}{8} = \dfrac{6}{8} = \dfrac{3}{4}$.

The solution checks. ■

Adding and Subtracting Decimals

Use place value to add and subtract decimal numbers.

Adding Whole Numbers and Decimals

How to Add Decimals

Vertical Addition

Step 1 Align the addends by place value.

Step 2 Add the digits in each place, beginning with the farthest place on the right and working to the left.

Step 3 If the sum of the digits in any place is greater than 9, regroup 10 units from that place as 1 unit in the next-greater place.

Tip Sometimes addends show different numbers of places to the right of the decimal point. When the number of places isn't the same, you may choose to write zeros to the right of the last place in the addend(s) that show fewer places.

EXAMPLE 1

Add. Use estimation to check that your answer is reasonable.

$$4.638 + 7.7$$

SOLUTION

Line up the numbers by place value. Use the equivalent decimal 7.700 so that the addends have the same number of digits to the right of the decimal point.

$$
\begin{array}{r}
\overset{1}{4}.638 \\
+\ 7.700 \\
\hline
12.338
\end{array}
$$

$$4.638 + 7.7 = 12.338$$

CHECK

Use estimation to check.

$$5 + 8 = 13 \checkmark$$

The answer is close to the estimate, so the answer is reasonable. ■

EXAMPLE 2

Stacy is weighing chemicals in a lab. The mass of Chemical A is 4.568 g, and the mass of Chemical B is 0.09 g. What is the total mass of the chemicals?

SOLUTION

Add. Line up the numbers by place value. Write a 0 in the thousandths place of 0.09.

$$
\begin{array}{r}
\overset{1}{4}.568 \\
+\ 0.090 \\
\hline
4.658
\end{array}
$$

The total mass of the chemicals is 4.658 g.

CHECK

Use estimation to check. Round each number to the nearest tenth, and then add.

$$4.6 + 0.1 = 4.7 \checkmark$$

The answer is close to the estimate, so the answer is reasonable. ■

Subtracting Whole Numbers and Decimals

How to Subtract Decimals

Vertical Subtraction

Step 1 Align the numbers by place value, with the greater number above the other.

Step 2 Subtract the digits in each place, beginning with the farthest place on the right and working to the left.

Step 3 If the greater digit is in the second number for any place value you are subtracting, then you must regroup.

Tip Record any regrouping carefully. You might need to regroup in the same place twice.

EXAMPLE 3

Subtract. Use estimation to check your answer.

$$8.23 - 4.77$$

SOLUTION

$$
\begin{array}{r}
\overset{7}{\cancel{8}}.\overset{11}{\cancel{2}}\overset{13}{\cancel{3}} \\
-\ 4.77 \\
\hline
3.46
\end{array}
$$

There are not enough hundredths to subtract, so regroup 1 tenth as 10 hundredths. Then regroup 1 one as 10 tenths.

$$8.23 - 4.77 = 3.46$$

CHECK
Use estimation to check.

$$8 - 5 = 3 \checkmark$$

The answer is close to the estimate, so the answer is reasonable. ▪

EXAMPLE 4

Subtract. Use estimation to check your answer.

$$12.004 - 5.57$$

▶ **Remember** Align numbers by place value. To do this, you can align the decimal points.

SOLUTION

$$
\begin{array}{r}
\overset{1\ \ 9\ 10}{12.00\cancel{0}4} \\
-\ 5.570 \\
\hline
6.434
\end{array}
$$

Write a 0 to fill the thousandths place of 5.57. Before subtracting, regroup 12.004 as 1 ten, 1 one, 9 tenths, 10 hundredths, and 4 thousandths.

$$12.004 - 5.57 = 6.434$$

CHECK

Use estimation to check. Round each number to the nearest whole, and then subtract.

$$12 - 6 = 6\ \checkmark$$

The answer is close to the estimate, so the answer is reasonable. ▪

EXAMPLE 5

Ben poured 14 mL of solution into a beaker. He poured 3.81 mL of the solution into a dish. How much solution is left in the beaker?

SOLUTION

$$
\begin{array}{r}
\overset{3\ \ 9\ 10}{1\cancel{4}.00} \\
-\ 3.81 \\
\hline
10.19
\end{array}
$$

Regroup 1 ten and 4 ones as 1 ten, 3 ones, 9 tenths, and 10 hundredths. Then subtract.

There are 10.19 mL of solution left in the beaker.

CHECK

Use estimation to check. Round each number to the nearest whole, and then subtract.

$$14 - 4 = 10\ \checkmark$$

The answer is close to the estimate, so the answer is reasonable. ▪

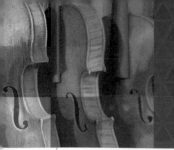

Multiplying and Dividing Decimals

Place value plays an important part in correctly determining products and quotients in decimal problems.

Multiplying Whole Numbers and Decimals

Definition
A **product** is the result of multiplying two or more factors.

How to Multiply Decimals
Vertical Multiplication **Step 1** Multiply the value of each digit in the second factor by each digit in the first factor. **Step 2** Place zeros to the right of each partial product to reflect the place value. **Step 3** Add all the partial products. **Step 4** Use estimation to check your answer. **Tip** When multiplying decimals, count the number of places to the right of the decimal point in each factor. The total tells you how many places are to the right of the decimal point in the product.

EXAMPLE 1

Multiply.

$$4.7 \bullet 2.9$$

SOLUTION

Count decimal places in the factors to know where to place the decimal point in the product.

$$
\begin{array}{r}
\overset{\overset{1}{6}}{4.7} \\
\times\ 2.9 \\
\hline
4\,2\,3 \\
+\,9\,4\,0 \\
\hline
1\,3.6\,3
\end{array}
$$

$$4.7 \bullet 2.9 = 13.63$$

CHECK

Use estimation to check.

$$5 \bullet 3 = 15 \ \checkmark$$

The answer is close to the estimate, so the answer is reasonable. ■

EXAMPLE 2

Tomatoes cost $1.75/lb. How much would 3.4 lb of tomatoes cost?

SOLUTION

$$
\begin{array}{r}
\overset{\overset{2\ \ 1}{3\ \ 2}}{1.75} \\
\times\ 3.4 \\
\hline
700 \\
+\,5250 \\
\hline
5.950
\end{array}
$$

Multiply 1.75 by 3.4.

Count decimal places in the factors to know where to place the decimal point in the product.

The cost for 3.4 lb of tomatoes is $5.95. ■

Dividing Whole Numbers and Decimals

How to Divide Numbers (Long Division)

Step 1 Divide the divisor into the first digits of the dividend.

Step 2 Multiply according to the place value of the digit you wrote in the quotient.

Step 3 Subtract the partial product.

Step 4 Divide the divisor into the difference.

Step 5 Repeat.

Tips When dividing, place digits exactly where they should be in the quotient. Be careful when you place the decimal point.

Always rewrite a decimal division problem as an equivalent problem with a whole-number divisor.

EXAMPLE 3

Divide.

$$67.2 \div 3.2$$

SOLUTION

First, write the problem as an equivalent problem with a whole-number divisor by multiplying both the divisor and dividend by 10.

$$67.2 \div 3.2 = 672 \div 32$$

$$
\begin{array}{r}
21 \\
32\overline{)672} \\
-640 \\
\hline
32 \\
-32 \\
\hline
0
\end{array}
$$

$$67.2 \div 3.2 = 21$$

CHECK

Multiply to check.

$$21 \cdot 3.2 = 67.2 \checkmark \ \blacksquare$$

EXAMPLE 4

Divide.

$$586.8 \div 18$$

▶ **Think About It** When dividing by 18, imagine dividing by a simpler number close to 18, such as 20.

SOLUTION

$$
\begin{array}{r}
32.6 \\
18\overline{)586.8} \\
-540.0 \\
\hline
46.8 \\
-36.0 \\
\hline
108 \\
-108 \\
\hline
0
\end{array}
$$

Divide as you would with whole numbers. Write the decimal point in the quotient.

$$586.8 \div 18 = 32.6$$

CHECK

Estimate to check.

$$30 \cdot 20 = 600 \checkmark$$

The answer is close to the estimate, so the answer is reasonable. ■

EXAMPLE 5

Divide.

$$97.768 \div 8.08$$

SOLUTION

$97.768 \div 8.08 = 9776.8 \div 808$ Write the problem as an equivalent problem with a whole-number divisor.

$$
\begin{array}{r}
12.1 \\
808\overline{)9776.8} \\
-8080.0 \\
\hline
1696.8 \\
-1616.0 \\
\hline
808 \\
-808 \\
\hline
0
\end{array}
$$

Divide. Write the decimal point in the quotient.

$$97.768 \div 8.08 = 12.1$$

▶ **Think About It** The answer is reasonable. To see if the answer is exactly correct, multiply 12.1 by 8.08 and see if the product is 97.768.

CHECK

Multiply to check.

$$8.08 \cdot 12.1 = 97.768 \checkmark \; ■$$

EXAMPLE 6

Divide.

$$11.44 \div 5.5$$

SOLUTION

$11.44 \div 5.5 = 114.4 \div 55$ Write the problem as an equivalent
problem with a whole-number divisor.

$$
\begin{array}{r}
2.08 \\
55\overline{)114.40} \\
-110.00 \\
\hline
4.40 \\
-0.00 \\
\hline
4.40 \\
-4.40 \\
\hline
0
\end{array}
$$

Divide. Write the decimal point in
the quotient.

$$11.44 \div 5.5 = 2.08$$

CHECK

Estimate to check.

$$2 \cdot 55 = 110 \checkmark$$

The answer is close to the estimate, so the answer is reasonable. ■

EXAMPLE 7

Sumaya is working in the science lab. She must separate 339.5 mL of
solution into batches of 24.25 mL. How many batches should she make?

SOLUTION

$339.5 \div 24.25 = 33,950 \div 2425$ Use division. Write the problem as
an equivalent problem with a whole-
number divisor.

$$
\begin{array}{r}
14 \\
2425\overline{)33950} \\
-24250 \\
\hline
9700 \\
-9700 \\
\hline
0
\end{array}
$$

Divide.

Sumaya should separate the solution into 14 batches. ■

EXAMPLE 8

Rahsaan did some shopping online. He ordered a desk for $724.55, a chair for $129.93, and 4 books for $19.99 each. If he makes equal monthly payments of $77.87, how long will it take him to pay for the order?

SOLUTION

$$\overset{3\,3\quad3}{19.99}$$
$$\underline{\times\qquad 4}$$
$$79.96$$

Find the amount he owes. Multiply 4 by 19.99 to find the amount he spent on books.

$$\overset{2\,2\quad1}{79.96}$$
$$724.55$$
$$\underline{+129.93}$$
$$934.44$$

Add the product to the amount he spent on the desk and chair.

He owes $934.44 in all.

$$934.44 \div 77.87 = 93,444 \div 7787$$

Divide $934.44 by $77.87 to find the number of months to pay it off.

$$
\begin{array}{r}
12 \\
7787\overline{)93444} \\
-77870 \\
\hline
15574 \\
-15574 \\
\hline
0
\end{array}
$$

After 12 monthly payments, the order will be paid in full. ■

Rational Numbers

Topic List

Businesspeople really care about positive and negative numbers—the difference between profit and loss. When you want to figure out how well a business is operating, positives and negatives will help.

Negative Numbers

If the temperature starts at 7°C and then drops by 12°C, the result is a negative temperature.

Locating Integers on a Number Line

You have seen number lines used to show counting numbers like 1, 2, 20, and maybe even 13,597. You can extend the number line in the direction that is on the opposite side of zero as well. When you do, call the counting numbers positive and the numbers on the opposite side of zero negative.

Definition
An **integer** is any whole number or its opposite. The integers: . . . −3, −2, −1, 0, 1, 2, 3, . . .

EXAMPLE 1

Identify the coordinate of point A.

SOLUTION

Look at the relationship between 0 and point A. Also look at the relationship of point A to the closest labeled integer.

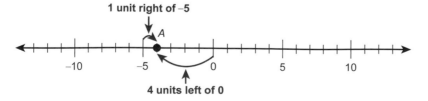

Point *A* is 4 units to the left of 0 and 1 unit to the right of −5. Both of these facts indicate that point *A* is located at −4.

The coordinate of point *A* is −4. ∎

Representing Situations Using Integers

The table shows some words representing positive and negative situations.

Words for Positive and Negative Situations	
Positive	**Negative**
up	down
increase	decrease
above	below
gain	loss
filling	emptying
rise	drop

EXAMPLE 2

Use an integer to represent the situation.

A The temperature rises 12°C.

SOLUTION
Rises indicates a positive integer.
+12 represents a rise of 12°C.

B A diver dives 43 ft below sea level.

SOLUTION
Below indicates a negative integer.
−43 represents a position of 43 ft below sea level. ∎

Rational Numbers on a Number Line

A number line goes in two directions. To the right of zero are positive numbers. To the left of zero are negative numbers.

Nonzero **opposites** are two numbers that are the same distance from zero on a number line. A number line can be used to compare and order numbers. Every number has its own corresponding point on a number line.

The set of integers is $\{\ldots, -3, -2, -1, 0, 1, 2, 3, \ldots\}$. It is the set of whole numbers and their opposites.

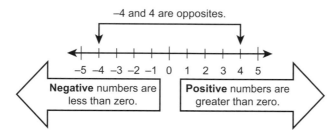

The opposite of zero is zero. Zero is neither positive nor negative.

▶ **Think About It** Zero is a whole number and an integer.

Identifying Coordinates of Points on a Number Line

A **coordinate** is a number that indicates the location of a point on a number line. The **origin** is the point on a number line with coordinate 0.

EXAMPLE 1

State the coordinate of each indicated point.

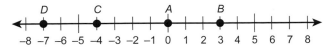

A point *A*

SOLUTION
Point *A* is the origin. The coordinate of point *A* is 0.

B point *B*

SOLUTION
Point *B* is 3 units to the right of the origin. The coordinate of point *B* is 3.

C point *C*

SOLUTION
Point *C* is 4 units to the left of the origin. The coordinate of point *C* is −4.

D point *D*

SOLUTION
Point *D* is 7 units to the left of the origin. The coordinate of point *D* is −7. ■

▶ **Think About It** A number with no symbol in front is positive. So 3 represents positive 3. You may sometimes see +3 to represent positive 3.

Graphing Rational Numbers

You can graph and name fractions and decimals on a number line.

EXAMPLE 2

Name the coordinates of points A, B, C, and D.

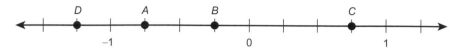

There are 4 spaces from 0 to 1 and from 0 to -1, so each unit on the number line represents $\frac{1}{4}$. Numbers to the left of 0 are negative, and numbers to the right of 0 are positive.

SOLUTION

Point A is 3 units to the left of 0, so it is located at $-\frac{3}{4}$.

Point B is 1 unit to the left of 0, so it is located at $-\frac{1}{4}$.

Point C is 3 units to the right of 0, so it is located at $\frac{3}{4}$.

Point D is 1 unit to the left of -1, so it is located at $-1\frac{1}{4}$. ■

EXAMPLE 3

Name the coordinates of points A, B, and C.

▶ **Think About It** There are 10 spaces from 0 to 1. Each space represents 0.1. Numbers to the left of 0 are negative.

SOLUTION

Point *A* is 2 units to the right of 0, so it is located at 0.2.

Point *B* is 6 units to the left of 0, so it is located at −0.6.

Point *C* is 7 units to the right of 0, so it is located at 0.7. ■

EXAMPLE 4

Graph each number on a number line.

A Plot *F* at $-1\frac{1}{2}$ and *G* at $\frac{5}{2}$.

SOLUTION

There is one tick mark between 0 and 1. So the distance between two tick

marks is $\frac{1}{2}$. Since $-1\frac{1}{2}$ is negative, plot *F* one space to the left of −1. To

plot *G*, start at 0 and count each tick mark as $\frac{1}{2}$. Stop when you get to 5 halves.

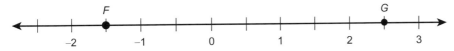

> **Think About It** Note that $1\frac{1}{2}$ is between 1 and 2. So $-1\frac{1}{2}$ is
> between −1 and −2.

B Plot *H* at 0.1 and *J* at −1.4.

SOLUTION

Since there are 5 spaces between −1 and 0, each space represents $\frac{1}{5}$, or

0.2 written in decimal form. Plot *H* a half-unit to the right of 0, since 0.1 is
halfway between 0 and 0.2. To plot *J*, start at −1.0 and move left 2 spaces.

Comparing and Ordering Rational Numbers

You can use a number line to compare and order rational numbers.

EXAMPLE 5

Restate the inequality as the position of the numbers on a number line.

A $-1\frac{1}{2} < -\frac{1}{2}$

> **Q&A**
>
> **Q** When comparing two numbers on a number line, how can you tell which number is greater?
>
> **A** The number on the right is always greater than the number on the left.

SOLUTION

Since $-1\frac{1}{2}$ is less than $-\frac{1}{2}$, $-1\frac{1}{2}$ is to the left of $-\frac{1}{2}$ on a number line.

B $0.3 > -1$

SOLUTION

Since 0.3 is greater than -1, 0.3 is to the right of -1 on a number line. ■

EXAMPLE 6

Compare the pair of numbers. Write $<$, $>$, or $=$.

A -1.4 and 0.4

SOLUTION

Plot the points on a number line.

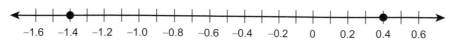

Since -1.4 is to the left of 0.4, $-1.4 < 0.4$.

B $-\dfrac{5}{8}$ and $-1\dfrac{3}{8}$

> **Remember** When comparing two negative numbers, the number closest to 0 is greater, since that number is farther to the right.

SOLUTION

Since $-\dfrac{5}{8}$ is to the right of -1 and $-1\dfrac{3}{8}$ is to the left of -1 on a number line, then $-\dfrac{5}{8}$ is to the right of $-1\dfrac{3}{8}$. Therefore $-\dfrac{5}{8} > -1\dfrac{3}{8}$. ■

EXAMPLE 7

Order the set of numbers from least to greatest.

A $\dfrac{2}{3}, -1\dfrac{1}{3}, 2$

SOLUTION

Plot the points on a number line.

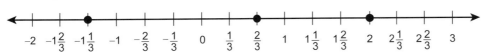

Record the numbers as they appear from left to right.

$$-1\dfrac{1}{3}, \dfrac{2}{3}, 2$$

B $-2.1, 2.2, 1.1$

SOLUTION

Since -2.1 is the only negative number, it is the least. Since 2.2 is greater than 1.1, it is the greatest. The order of the numbers from least to greatest is $-2.1, 1.1, 2.2$. ■

EXAMPLE 8

A On a winter day, the temperature was −10.5°F in New York and 14.3°F in Charlotte. Which city recorded a colder temperature?

SOLUTION

Since −10.5 is less than 0 and 14.3 is greater than 0, −10.5 < 14.3. It was colder in New York.

B The elevation of San Francisco is 55 ft. The elevation of New Orleans is −6.5 ft. The elevation of Miami is 5.9 ft. List the cities in order from highest to lowest elevation.

SOLUTION

Since New Orleans has a negative elevation, it has the lowest elevation. Since 55 is greater than 5.9, 55 ft is the greatest. The cities in order from highest to lowest elevation are San Francisco, Miami, and New Orleans. ▪

Absolute Value and Opposites

You can use absolute value to determine distances along a number line. Opposites are numbers on a number line that are the same distance from zero.

Absolute Value

The **absolute value** of a number is its distance from zero. Absolute value is indicated by the | | symbol. For example, read |−4| as "the absolute value of negative four."

EXAMPLE 1

A Find $|-4|$.

SOLUTION

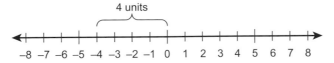

Since −4 is 4 units from zero, $|-4| = 4$.

B Find $|6|$.

SOLUTION

Since 6 is 6 units from zero, $|6| = 6$. ▪

EXAMPLE 2

A Find $\left|-\dfrac{3}{4}\right|$.

SOLUTION

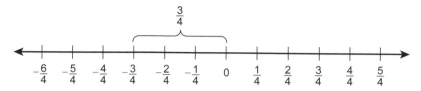

Since $-\dfrac{3}{4}$ is $\dfrac{3}{4}$ from 0, $\left|-\dfrac{3}{4}\right| = \dfrac{3}{4}$.

B Find $|1.2|$.

SOLUTION

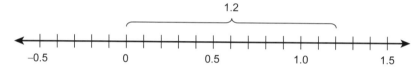

Since 1.2 is 1.2 from 0, $|1.2| = 1.2$. ■

Comparing and Ordering Absolute Value Expressions

You can compare and order absolute value expressions. Simplify first, and then compare.

EXAMPLE 3

Compare. Write $<$, $>$, or $=$.

A $|3|$ and $|-4|$

SOLUTION

$|3| = 3$ Simplify the expressions.

$|-4| = 4$

Since $3 < 4$, $|3| < |-4|$.   Compare.

B $\left|-\frac{1}{2}\right|$ and $\left|-2\frac{1}{2}\right|$

SOLUTION

$\left|-\frac{1}{2}\right| = \frac{1}{2}$ Simplify the expressions.

$\left|-2\frac{1}{2}\right| = 2\frac{1}{2}$

Since $\frac{1}{2} < 2\frac{1}{2}$, $\left|-\frac{1}{2}\right| < \left|-2\frac{1}{2}\right|$.   Compare.

C $|-2.2|$ and $|1.5|$

SOLUTION

$|-2.2| = 2.2$ Simplify the expressions.

$|1.5| = 1.5$

Since $2.2 > 1.5$, $|-2.2| > |1.5|$.   Compare. ■

EXAMPLE 4

Order the set of numbers from least to greatest.

A $|7|$, $|-2|$, and $|-10|$

SOLUTION

$|7| = 7$ Simplify the expressions.

$|-2| = 2$

$|-10| = 10$

Since $2 < 7 < 10$, the order from least to greatest is $|-2|$, $|7|$, and $|-10|$.

B $\left|-\dfrac{7}{2}\right|, \left|\dfrac{5}{2}\right|,$ and $\left|-\dfrac{3}{2}\right|$

SOLUTION

$\left|-\dfrac{7}{2}\right| = \dfrac{7}{2}$ Simplify the expressions.

$\left|\dfrac{5}{2}\right| = \dfrac{5}{2}$

$\left|-\dfrac{3}{2}\right| = \dfrac{3}{2}$

Since $\dfrac{3}{2} < \dfrac{5}{2} < \dfrac{7}{2}$, the order from least to greatest is $\left|-\dfrac{3}{2}\right|, \left|\dfrac{5}{2}\right|,$ and $\left|-\dfrac{7}{2}\right|$.

C $|2.8|, |-2.7|,$ and $|0|$

SOLUTION

$|2.8| = 2.8$ Simplify the expressions.

$|-2.7| = 2.7$

$|0| = 0$

Since $0 < 2.7 < 2.8$, the order from least to greatest is $|0|, |-2.7|,$ and $|2.8|$. ■

Opposite Numbers

Numbers are opposites if they are the same distance from zero, but in different directions on a number line. Another property of opposites is that they have different signs (except for zero), but the same absolute value. For example, 12 and -12 are opposites because they have different signs, but $|12| = 12$ and $|-12| = 12$.

> ▶ **Think About It** The same sign is used for opposite, negative, and subtraction.

The $-$ sign is used to indicate opposite. You can read -2 as either "negative two" or the "opposite of two." Read $-(-2)$ as the "opposite of negative two." The opposite of -2 is 2, so write $-(-2) = 2$ and read it as the "opposite of negative two equals two."

▶ **Think About It** All numbers have opposites, not just integers. For example, the opposite of 3.4 is -3.4.

EXAMPLE 5

Write the opposite of the integer.

A 3

SOLUTION
The opposite of 3 is -3.

B -10

SOLUTION
The opposite of -10 is 10. Or, $-(-10) = 10$.

C 0

SOLUTION
The opposite of 0 is 0. ▪

Interpreting Opposite Numbers

You can use opposite numbers to interpret real-world situations.

EXAMPLE 6

A Patrick sends $20.13 from his bank account to Jenny's bank account. What is the change in value in each person's bank account?

SOLUTION

Since Patrick sends money from his account, the change in value is −$20.13.

Since Jenny receives money in her account, the change in value is the opposite, $20.13.

B A bird is 8 ft above sea level, while a fish has the opposite elevation. What is the elevation of each?

SOLUTION

Sea level is 0. The bird is at 8 or +8 ft, while the fish is at −8 ft. ∎

Absolute Value and Distance

You can use a simple formula to find the distance between any two points on a line.

Finding the Absolute Value and the Opposite of an Integer

The **absolute value** of an integer is its distance from the origin, or 0, on the number line. The absolute value of a is written $|a|$.

Opposites are pairs of numbers whose distance from 0 is the same.

▶ **Think About It** You can easily find a number's opposite by changing its sign.

To find the opposite and the absolute value of an integer, use the distance the integer is from 0 on the number line.

EXAMPLE 1

Find the absolute value and the opposite of the integer.

A 7

SOLUTION
Draw a number line and locate 7. To find the absolute value of 7, find the distance from 7 to 0. To find the opposite of 7, find the other number that is the same distance from 0.

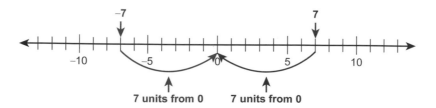

7 units from 0   7 units from 0

7 is 7 units from 0. The other number that is 7 units from 0 is -7.
$|7| = 7$ and the opposite of 7 is -7.

> **Think About It** A number without any sign is assumed to be positive. So 7 is the same as $+7$.

B -9

SOLUTION

-9 is 9 units from 0. The other number that is 9 units from 0 is 9. $|-9| = 9$ and the opposite of -9 is 9. ∎

Finding Distance

You can use the formula to find the distance between two points on the number line.

Distance Between Two Points

The distance d between two points with coordinates a and b on a number line can be found using

$$d = |b - a|.$$

EXAMPLE 2

Find the distance between the two points on the number line.

SOLUTION

Use the formula.

$$d = |b - a|$$
$$ = |12 - 3| \qquad \text{Replace } b \text{ with 12 and } a \text{ with 3.}$$
$$ = |9| \qquad\quad\ \text{Simplify.}$$
$$ = 9$$

The distance between the two points is 9 units. ▪

> ▶ **Think About It** It doesn't matter which point you select for *a* and which you select for *b*. The answer is the same.
>
> $$|3 - 12| = |-9| = 9$$

Application: Finding Locations

EXAMPLE 3

Ken hooked his dog's 7 ft leash on a fence. The number line represents the fence with 1 unit = 1 ft. The point is where Ken hooked the leash. Where are the farthest locations that Ken's dog can go along the fence?

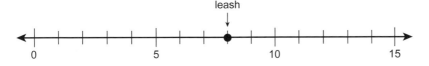

SOLUTION

The leash is 7 ft long. Since Ken hooked the leash at the 8 ft location, subtract 7 from 8 and add 7 to 8.

$$8 - 7 = 1 \qquad \text{and} \qquad 8 + 7 = 15$$

The farthest locations along the fence that Ken's dog can go are at 1 ft and 15 ft. ▪

Points on a Coordinate Plane

You can use a single number to describe the location of a point on a line, but on a coordinate plane it takes two numbers to describe the location of any point.

Identifying Axes and Quadrants

A **coordinate plane** is formed by two perpendicular number lines called **axes**. The *x*-axis is a horizontal line. The *y*-axis is a vertical line. The axes intersect at the point at which they both have coordinate zero. This point is called the origin. The axes separate the plane into four **quadrants**. On the axes, positive *x* goes right and positive *y* goes up. Negative *x* goes left and negative *y* goes down.

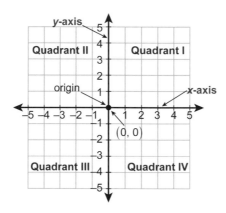

EXAMPLE 1

For each point, name the axis it is on or the quadrant it lies in.

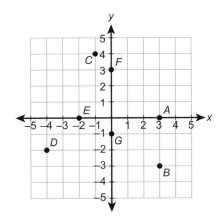

SOLUTION

Points *A* and *E* lie on the *x*-axis.

Points *F* and *G* lie on the *y*-axis.

Point *C* lies in Quadrant II.

Point *D* lies in Quadrant III.

Point *B* lies in Quadrant IV. ■

Using an Ordered Pair to Describe a Location

To describe the location of a point, use an **ordered pair**. An ordered pair has the form (x, y). The number x (the **x-coordinate**) describes the point's horizontal (left-right) distance from the origin. The number y (the **y-coordinate**) describes the point's vertical (up-down) distance from the origin. The numbers in an ordered pair are called coordinates.

To name the coordinates of a point, determine how you can get to the point from the origin by first counting right or left and then counting up or down.

EXAMPLE 2

Name the ordered pair for the point.

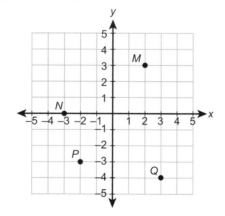

A point M

SOLUTION

Start at the origin.
Go **2** units to the right.
Go **3** units up.

The ordered pair for point M is $(2, 3)$.

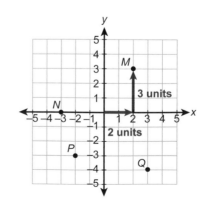

B point *N*

SOLUTION

Start at the origin.

Go **3** units to the left.

Go **0** units vertically (up or down).

The ordered pair for point *N* is $(-3, 0)$.

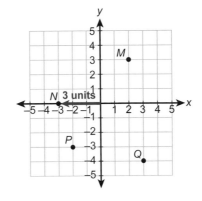

C point *P*

SOLUTION

Start at the origin.

Go **2** units to the left.

Go **3** units down.

The ordered pair for point *P* is $(-2, -3)$.

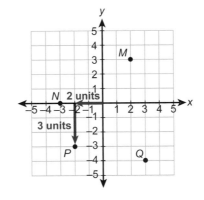

D point *Q*

SOLUTION

Start at the origin.

Go **3** units to the right.

Go **4** units down.

The ordered pair for point *Q* is $(3, -4)$.

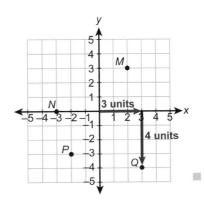

▶ **Remember** The signs for the directions are + for right and up and − for left and down.

EXAMPLE 3

Name the ordered pair for the point.

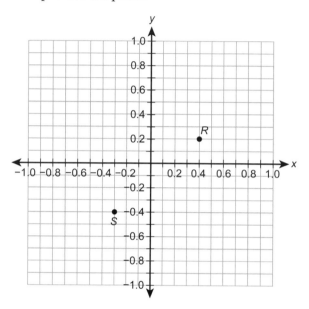

A point R

SOLUTION

Start at the origin.

Go **0.4** units to the right.

Go **0.2** units up.

The ordered pair for point R is $(0.4, 0.2)$.

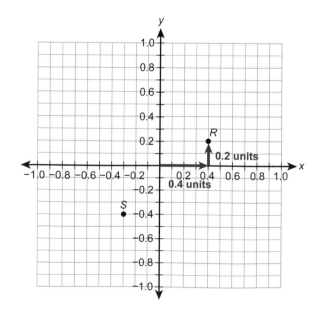

B point *S*

SOLUTION

Start at the origin.

Go **0.3** units to the left.

Go **0.4** units down.

The ordered pair for point *S* is $(-0.3, -0.4)$.

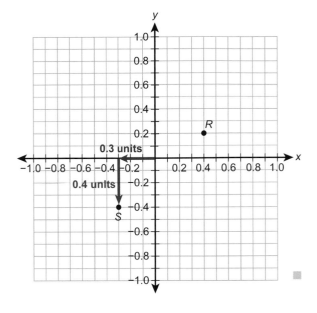

EXAMPLE 4

Name the ordered pair for the point as a fraction.

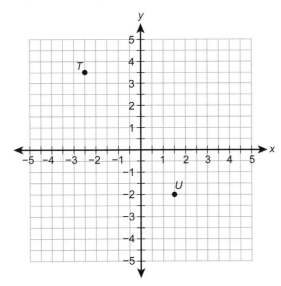

A point T

SOLUTION

Start at the origin.

Go $2\frac{1}{2}$ units to the left.

Go $3\frac{1}{2}$ units up.

The ordered pair for point T is $\left(-2\frac{1}{2}, 3\frac{1}{2}\right)$.

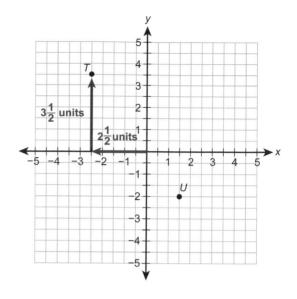

▶ **Remember** Always double-check your positive and negative signs.

B point U

SOLUTION

Start at the origin.

Go $1\frac{1}{2}$ units to the right.

Go **2** units down.

The ordered pair for point U is $\left(1\frac{1}{2}, -2\right)$.

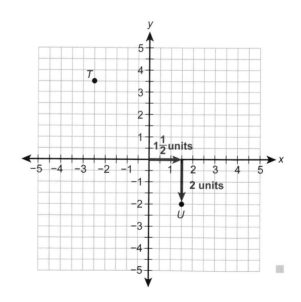

Graphing an Ordered Pair

EXAMPLE 5

Graph the ordered pair on the coordinate plane.

> ▶ **Remember** A point is the graph of an ordered pair. An ordered pair contains the coordinates of a point.

A $(-1, 4)$

SOLUTION
Start at the origin.
The x-coordinate is -1.
Go **1** unit left.
The y-coordinate is 4.
Go **4** units up.
Draw and label a dot.

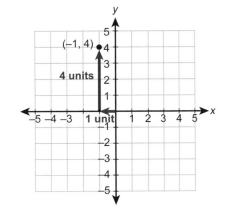

B $(0, -3)$

SOLUTION
Start at the origin.
The x-coordinate is 0, so do not move left or right.
The y-coordinate is -3.
Go **3** units down.
Draw and label a dot.

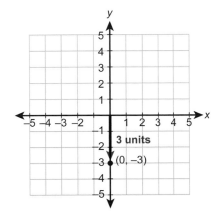

C $(4, -4)$

SOLUTION

Start at the origin.

The x-coordinate is 4.

Go **4** units right.

The y-coordinate is −4.

Go **4** units down.

Draw and label a dot.

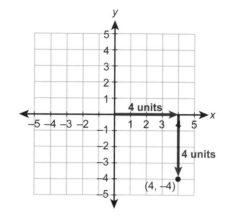

D $(-0.6, 0.2)$

SOLUTION

Start at the origin.

The x-coordinate is −0.6.

Go **0.6** units to the left.

The y-coordinate is 0.2.

Go **0.2** units up.

Draw and label a dot.

E $(-1.8, -1.2)$

SOLUTION

Start at the origin.

The x-coordinate is -1.8.

Go **1.8** units to the left.

The y-coordinate is -1.2.

Go **1.2** units down.

Draw and label a dot.

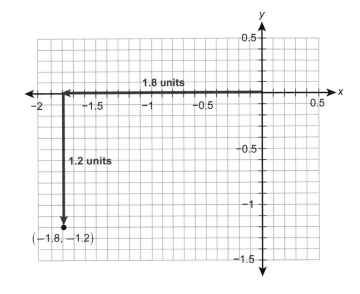

F $\left(2\frac{2}{3}, 1\frac{1}{3}\right)$

SOLUTION

Start at the origin.

The x-coordinate is $2\frac{2}{3}$.

Go $2\frac{2}{3}$ units to the right.

The y-coordinate is $1\frac{1}{3}$.

Go $1\frac{1}{3}$ units up.

Draw and label a dot.

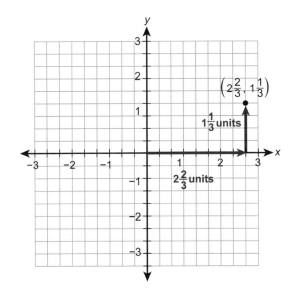

G $\left(1, -\frac{1}{3}\right)$

SOLUTION

Start at the origin.

The *x*-coordinate is 1.

Go **1** unit to the right.

The *y*-coordinate is $-\frac{1}{3}$.

Go $\frac{1}{3}$ units down.

Draw and label a dot.

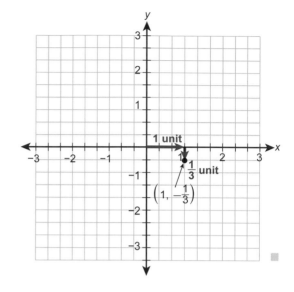

Distance in the Coordinate Plane

You can find the distance between two points by using their coordinates.
When *x*-coordinates are the same, the points fall on the same vertical line.
When *y*-coordinates are the same, the points fall on the same horizontal line.

EXAMPLE 6

Find the distance between the ordered pairs.

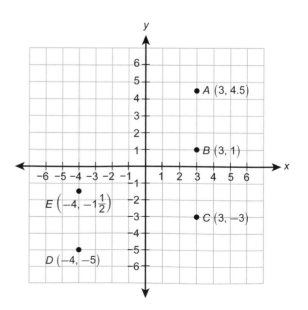

A *A* and *B*

SOLUTION

▶ **Think About It** Focus on *A* and *B*. Imagine connecting them to form a vertical line. The length of segment *AB* is the distance between the points. Count units to check your answer.

The *x*-coordinates are the same. The points fall on a vertical line. The *y*-coordinates are both positive. Subtract the lesser *y*-coordinate from the greater *y*-coordinate.

$$4.5 - 1 = 3.5$$

The points are 3.5 units apart.

B *D* and *E*

SOLUTION

The *x*-coordinates are the same. The *y*-coordinates are both negative.

Find the distance from each *y*-coordinate to the *x*-axis.

E is $1\frac{1}{2}$ units from the *x*-axis. *D* is 5 units from the *x*-axis.

Subtract the lesser distance from the greater distance.

$$5 - 1\frac{1}{2} = 3\frac{1}{2}$$

The points are $3\frac{1}{2}$ units apart.

C *B* and *C*

SOLUTION

The *x*-coordinates are the same. The *y*-coordinates have different signs.

Find the distance from each *y*-coordinate to the *x*-axis.

C is 3 units from the *x*-axis. *B* is 1 unit from the *x*-axis on the other side of the axis.

Add the distances.

$$3 + 1 = 4$$

The points are 4 units apart. ■

▶ Q&A

Q Start at *C* and move up to *B*. How many units do you move?

A 4 units

EXAMPLE 7

Find the distance between the ordered pairs.

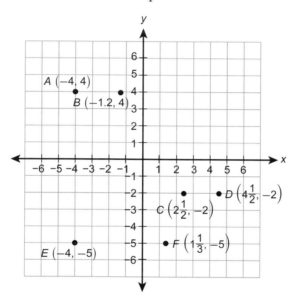

A *C* and *D*

SOLUTION

The *y*-coordinates are the same. The points fall on a horizontal line. The *x*-coordinates are both positive. Subtract the lesser *x*-coordinate from the greater *x*-coordinate.

$$4\frac{1}{2} - 2\frac{1}{2} = 2$$

The points are 2 units apart.

B *A* and *B*

SOLUTION

The *y*-coordinates are the same. The *x*-coordinates are both negative.

Find the distance from each *x*-coordinate to the *y*-axis.

A is 4 units from the *y*-axis. *B* is 1.2 units from the *y*-axis.

Subtract the distances.

$$4 - 1.2 = 2.8$$

The points are 2.8 units apart.

C *E* and *F*

SOLUTION

The *y*-coordinates are the same. The *x*-coordinates are both negative.

Find the distance from each *x*-coordinate to the *y*-axis.

E is 4 units from the *y*-axis. *F* is $1\frac{1}{3}$ units from the *y*-axis on the other side of the axis.

Add the distances.

$$4 + 1\frac{1}{3} = 5\frac{1}{3}$$

The points are $5\frac{1}{3}$ units apart. ▪

Problem Solving in the Coordinate Plane

You can use the coordinate plane to help you solve real-world problems.

EXAMPLE 8

A On an imaginary grid on the golf course, a golf ball rolls from $(13, -2)$ to $(-15, -2)$. How many units did the golf ball roll?

SOLUTION

The y-coordinates are the same. The x-coordinates have different signs.

Find the distance from each x-coordinate to 0.

The ball started 13 units from the y-axis. It stopped 15 units from the y-axis on the other side of the y-axis.

Add, since the two points are on opposite sides of the y-axis.

$$13 + 15 = 28$$

The golf ball rolled 28 units.

B A cargo plane traveling from New York to Florida is plotted on a map. The starting point is at coordinates $(12.5, 9.6)$ on the map and the ending point at $(12.5, 53.1)$. How many vertical units on the map did the plane travel?

SOLUTION

The x-coordinates are the same. The y-coordinates are both positive. Subtract the lesser y-coordinate from the greater y-coordinate.

$$53.1 - 9.6 = 43.5$$

The plane traveled 43.5 units on the map.

C Jason's apartment is located at $\left(12\frac{3}{8}, -4\frac{5}{8}\right)$ on a map. His office is located at $\left(12\frac{3}{8}, -1\frac{5}{8}\right)$. How many units on the map is the distance from Jason's home to his work?

SOLUTION

The x-coordinates are the same. The y-coordinates are both negative.

Find each point's distance from the x-axis.

$\left(12\frac{3}{8}, -4\frac{5}{8}\right)$ is $4\frac{5}{8}$ units from the x-axis.

$\left(12\frac{3}{8}, -1\frac{5}{8}\right)$ is $1\frac{5}{8}$ units from the x-axis.

Subtract the distances.

$$4\frac{5}{8} - 1\frac{5}{8} = 3$$

The distance between Jason's home and work is 3 units on the map. ◼

Expressions

Topic List

How much wood is needed to build a fence? How much paint will it take to cover the fence? Translating words into math expressions can help solve problems like these.

Positive Exponents

A **power** is a special kind of product.

A power has a **base** and an **exponent**. In the power a^n, a is the base and n is the exponent. Read a^n as "a to the nth power." You can read a^2 as "a squared" and a^3 as "a cubed."

▶ **Think About It** Exponents are normally written above and to the right of the base.

Simplify a power by multiplying. The exponent tells how many times to use the base as a factor.

Positive Exponents

For any real number a and natural number n,

$$a^n = \underbrace{a \cdot a \cdot a \cdot a \cdot \ldots \cdot a}_{n \text{ factors}}$$

Simplifying Powers

EXAMPLE 1

Simplify.

A 2^4

SOLUTION

$2^4 = 2 \cdot 2 \cdot 2 \cdot 2$ Use 2 as a factor 4 times.

    $= 16$ Multiply.

B 0.4^2

SOLUTION

$0.4^2 = 0.4 \cdot 0.4$ Use 0.4 as a factor 2 times.

    $= 0.16$ Multiply the factors.

> ▶ **Think About It** Writing a power as a product first will help you avoid mistakes. In Example 1B, write $0.4 \cdot 0.4$, then multiply.

C $\left(\dfrac{1}{2}\right)^5$

SOLUTION

$\left(\dfrac{1}{2}\right)^5 = \dfrac{1}{2} \cdot \dfrac{1}{2} \cdot \dfrac{1}{2} \cdot \dfrac{1}{2} \cdot \dfrac{1}{2}$ Use $\dfrac{1}{2}$ as a factor 5 times.

    $= \dfrac{1}{32}$ Multiply. ▪

Exponents 0 and 1

Exponents 0 and 1

For all nonzero a,

$$a^0 = 1$$
$$a^1 = a$$

Because an expression can have only one value, mathematicians have agreed on a process to follow so that everyone simplifies expressions the same way. This process is the **order of operations**.

Order of Operations

Step 1   Perform operations within grouping symbols. For nested grouping symbols, simplify in the innermost group first.

Step 2   Evaluate powers (as indicated by exponents).

Step 3   Multiply and divide from left to right.

Step 4   Add and subtract from left to right.

EXAMPLE 2

Simplify.

A $4^0 \cdot 3^3$

SOLUTION

$$4^0 \cdot 3^3 = \mathbf{1} \cdot 3^3 \qquad \text{Use } a^0 = 1 \text{ to simplify } 4^0.$$

$$= 1 \cdot \mathbf{3} \cdot \mathbf{3} \cdot \mathbf{3} \qquad \text{Use 3 as a factor 3 times.}$$

$$= 27 \qquad \text{Multiply.}$$

B $(9 - 6)^2 + 2^1$

SOLUTION

$$(9 - 6)^2 + 2^1 = 3^2 + 2^1 \qquad \text{Subtract inside the parentheses.}$$

$$= \mathbf{9} + 2^1 \qquad \text{Simplify } 3^2.$$

$$= 9 + \mathbf{2} \qquad \text{Simplify } 2^1.$$

$$= 11 \qquad \text{Add.}$$

C -4^2

SOLUTION

$-4^2 = -(4 \cdot 4)$ Use 4 as a factor 2 times.

$ = -(16)$ Find the opposite of 16.

$ = -16$ Simplify. ■

> ▶ **Remember** Remember that a negative symbol can mean "opposite."

Writing a Number as a Power

When a number can be written in the form a^n (where n is an integer), the number is a power of a.

EXAMPLE 3

A Write 16 as a power of 2.

SOLUTION

$16 = 2 \cdot 2 \cdot 2 \cdot 2$ Use 2 as a factor 4 times.

$ = 2^4$ Write using an exponent.

> ▶ **Think About It** Divide the final product, 16, by the base, 2, and then divide the quotient by 2 again. Repeat until the final quotient is 1. The number of times the division is carried out is the exponent. This process is called repeated division.

B Write 125 as a power of 5.

SOLUTION

$125 = 5 \cdot 5 \cdot 5$ Use 5 as a factor 3 times.

$ = 5^3$ Write using an exponent. ■

Evaluating Expressions with Variables and Exponents

To evaluate an expression with variables, first substitute the given values. Then simplify using the order of operations.

EXAMPLE 4

Evaluate.

A $6b^3$ when $b = 4$

SOLUTION

$$6b^3 \quad = 6 \cdot 4^3 \qquad \text{Substitute 4 for } b.$$

$$= 6 \cdot 64 \qquad \text{Evaluate } 4^3.$$

$$= 384 \qquad \text{Multiply.}$$

> ▶ **Think About It** Unless it appears after parentheses, an exponent applies only to a single number or variable.
> $$6b^3 = 6 \cdot b \cdot b \cdot b$$
> On the other hand,
> $$(6b)^3 = (6b) \cdot (6b) \cdot (6b)$$

B $4m^3n^2$ when $m = 2$ and $n = 5$

SOLUTION

$$4m^3n^2 = 4 \cdot 2^3 \cdot 5^2 \qquad \text{Substitute 2 for } m \text{ and 5 for } n.$$

$$= 4 \cdot 8 \cdot 25 \qquad \text{Evaluate } 2^3 \text{ and } 5^2.$$

$$= 800 \qquad \text{Multiply.}$$

C $2x^3y^2$ when $x = 3$ and $y = 0.4$

SOLUTION

$$2x^3y^2 = 2 \cdot 3^3 \cdot 0.4^2 \qquad \text{Substitute 3 for } x \text{ and 0.4 for } y.$$

$$= 2 \cdot 27 \cdot 0.16 \qquad \text{Evaluate } 3^3 \text{ and } 0.4^2.$$

$$= 8.64 \qquad \text{Multiply. } \blacksquare$$

Application: Genealogy

EXAMPLE 5

You can use exponents to model the number of ancestors in each generation of a person's family tree.

In this family tree, M stands for "Mother" and F stands for "Father."

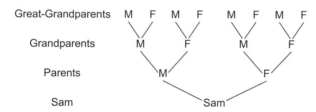

A How many people are 1 generation above Sam in the family tree? Write the number as a power of 2.

SOLUTION

There are 2 people. Sam's **2** parents are **1** generation above Sam.

$$2 = 2^1$$

B How many people are 2 generations above Sam in the family tree? Write the number as a power of 2.

SOLUTION

There are 4 people. Sam's **4** grandparents are **2** generations above Sam.

$$4 = 2^2$$

C Use the pattern to predict. How many people were in the sixth generation above Sam?

SOLUTION

There are 2^n people in the generation that is n generations above Sam. So there are 2^6 or 64 people in that generation. Sam has 64 great-great-great-great-grandparents. ■

Numerical Expressions

A **numerical expression** consists of numbers and one or more operations.

Here are some examples of numerical expressions.

$$18 - 2 \qquad 7 + 2 \cdot 3 \qquad 4 + 2\big[3 - 4 \div (12 - 8)\big] \qquad \frac{(5+3)^2}{10 - 3(4 - 2)}$$

▶ **Think About It**

NOTATION 8^2 An exponent indicates repeated multiplication, so $8^2 = 8 \cdot 8$.

To find the value of a numerical expression, you need to simplify the expression or evaluate the expression. To simplify a numerical expression, perform the indicated operation(s).

Consider the expression $7 + 2 \cdot 3$. If you add and then multiply, you get the value 27. But if you multiply and then add, you get the value 13.

So the correct way to simplify $7 + 2 \cdot 3$ is to multiply and then add.

$$7 + 2 \cdot 3 = 7 + 6 = 13$$

The most common grouping symbols are parentheses ( ). Grouping symbols can affect the value of an expression. Nested grouping symbols (grouping symbols within grouping symbols) contain brackets [ ] and sometimes braces { }.

Simplifying Expressions With and Without Grouping Symbols

EXAMPLE 1

Simplify.

A $5 \cdot 2 + 7$

SOLUTION

$$5 \cdot 2 + 7 = \mathbf{10} + 7 \qquad \text{Multiply.}$$
$$= 17 \qquad \text{Add.}$$

B $5 \cdot (2 + 7)$

SOLUTION

$$5 \cdot (2 + 7) = 5 \cdot (\mathbf{9}) \qquad \text{Add first because addition appears inside parentheses.}$$
$$= 45 \qquad \text{Multiply.} \ ▪$$

> ▶ **Think About It** The expression $5 \cdot (2 + 7)$ is also written as $5(2 + 7)$.

Simplifying Expressions with Several Operations

EXAMPLE 2

Simplify.

A $3 \cdot 7 - 10 \div 2 \cdot 3$

SOLUTION

$$3 \cdot 7 - 10 \div 2 \cdot 3 = \mathbf{21} - 10 \div 2 \cdot 3$$ Multiply and divide in order from left to right.

$$= 21 - \mathbf{5} \cdot 3$$

$$= 21 - \mathbf{15}$$

$$= 6$$ Subtract.

B $4 + 2\left[3 - 4 \div (12 - 8)\right]$

SOLUTION

$$4 + 2\left[3 - 4 \div (12 - 8)\right] = 4 + 2\left[3 - 4 \div \mathbf{4}\right]$$ Parentheses are nested within brackets. Subtract.

$$= 4 + 2\left[3 - \mathbf{1}\right]$$ Divide inside the brackets.

$$= 4 + 2\left[\mathbf{2}\right]$$ Subtract inside the brackets.

$$= 4 + \mathbf{4}$$ Multiply.

$$= 8$$ Add. ■

Simplifying an Expression with a Fraction Bar

A fraction bar indicates division. It is also a grouping symbol, separating the numerator from the denominator.

EXAMPLE 3

Simplify.

$$\frac{(5+3)^2}{1+2^5-23}$$

SOLUTION

Treat the fraction bar as a grouping symbol. Simplify the numerator and denominator, and then divide.

$\dfrac{(5+3)^2}{1+2^5-23} = \dfrac{(8)^2}{1+2^5-23}$ Perform the operation inside the parentheses.

$= \dfrac{64}{1+32-23}$ Evaluate powers: $8^2 = 8 \cdot 8 = 64$ and $2^5 = 2 \cdot 2 \cdot 2 \cdot 2 \cdot 2 = 32$.

$= \dfrac{64}{10}$ Add and subtract from left to right to simplify the denominator.

$= \dfrac{32}{5}$

$= 6.4$ Simplify. ■

▶ **Think About It** The expression can also be written as $(5+3)^2 \div (1+2^5-23)$.

Placing Grouping Symbols to Get a Specified Value

You can get different values for an expression by changing the placement of grouping symbols.

EXAMPLE 4

Place grouping symbols in the expression $2 \cdot 8 + 2^3 \cdot 10$ to get expressions that have these values: 20,000 and 80,000.

SOLUTION

The method is trial-and-error. Some possible placements of grouping symbols are $2 \cdot (8 + 2)^3 \cdot 10$, $\left[2 \cdot (8 + 2)\right]^3 \cdot 10$, and $(2 \cdot 8 + 2)^3 \cdot 10$. Evaluate these expressions, and try other placements if necessary. The two correct expressions are shown.

$$2 \cdot (8 + 2)^3 \cdot 10 = 2 \cdot (\mathbf{10})^3 \cdot 10$$
Perform the operation inside the parentheses.

$$= 2 \cdot \mathbf{1000} \cdot 10$$
Evaluate the power: $10^3 = 10 \cdot 10 \cdot 10 = 1000$.

$$= \mathbf{2000} \cdot 10$$
Multiply from left to right.

$$= 20{,}000$$
Multiply.

$$\left[2 \cdot (8 + 2)\right]^3 \cdot 10 = \left[2 \cdot (\mathbf{10})\right]^3 \cdot 10$$
Perform the operation inside the parentheses.

$$= \left[\mathbf{20}\right]^3 \cdot 10$$
Perform the operation inside the brackets.

$$= \mathbf{8000} \cdot 10$$
Evaluate the power: $20^3 = 20 \cdot 20 \cdot 20 = 8000$.

$$= 80{,}000$$
Multiply. ■

Variables

A **variable** is a symbol that represents a value.

Variables are usually represented by lowercase letters in italics. A **variable expression** is a combination of variables, numbers, and operations. Here are examples of variable expressions.

$$x - 2 \qquad 5n + 7 \qquad \frac{c + 1}{d - 2} \qquad 2y - 21z + 6$$

Unlike numerical expressions, to evaluate variable expressions, **substitute**, or replace, numbers for the variables. So the value of a variable expression depends on the numbers chosen for the variable(s).

▶ **Think About It** A variable expression can also be called an algebraic expression.

Evaluating Variable Expressions

To **evaluate** a variable expression, replace all the variables in the expression with numbers and simplify the resulting numerical expression.

EXAMPLE 1

Evaluate.

A $5n + 7$ when $n = 8$

> ▶ **Think About It**
>
> NOTATION $5n$ When a number and variable are written together, the operation is multiplication, so $5n = 5 \cdot n$.

SOLUTION

$$5n + 7 = 5 \cdot 8 + 7 \qquad \text{Substitute 8 for } n.$$

$$= 40 + 7 \qquad \text{Multiply.}$$

$$= 47 \qquad \text{Add.}$$

B $\dfrac{c + 1}{d - 2}$ when $c = 3$ and $d = 4$

SOLUTION

$$\frac{c + 1}{d - 2} = \frac{3 + 1}{4 - 2} \qquad \text{Substitute 3 for } c \text{ and 4 for } d.$$

$$= \frac{4}{2} \qquad \text{Simplify the numerator and then the denominator.}$$

$$= 2 \qquad \text{Divide.} \ \blacksquare$$

Identifying Terms

Variable expressions consist of terms. **Terms** are the parts of an expression that are added or subtracted. A term that has no variables is a **constant**.

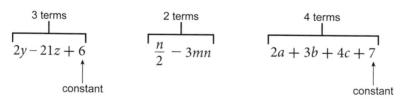

> ▶ **Remember** A constant is a term.

EXAMPLE 2

Identify the terms of the expression $3x + y + 23$.

SOLUTION
Each term is separated by a $+$. The terms are $3x$, y, and 23. The number 23 is a constant since there is no variable. ■

Identifying Coefficients and Factors

Terms can consist of two or more **factors**. The numerical part of a term is the **coefficient**. When the coefficient of a term is 1, it is usually not written.

> ▶ **Remember** In $2 \cdot 3 = 6$, 2 and 3 are called factors and 6 is called the product.

EXAMPLE 3

Identify the coefficient and factors of the term.

A $-mn$

SOLUTION
You can write the term $-mn$ as $-1 \cdot m \cdot n$. So the coefficient is -1. The factors are -1, m, and n.

B $\dfrac{n}{2}$

SOLUTION
You can write the term $\dfrac{n}{2}$ as $\dfrac{1}{2} \cdot n$. So the coefficient is $\dfrac{1}{2}$. The factors are $\dfrac{1}{2}$ and n. ■

Applications: Measurement and Distance Traveled

You can use expressions to solve many types of problems, including those involving measurement.

EXAMPLE 4

A Natalie jogged once around the perimeter of a football field, which has a length of 100 yd and a width of 60 yd. Find the total number of yards she jogged.

SOLUTION

Use the expression $2l + 2w$, where l is the length of the rectangle and w is the width of the rectangle, to find the perimeter. Evaluate $2l + 2w$ when $l = 100$ and $w = 60$.

$2l + 2w = 2 \cdot \mathbf{100} + 2 \cdot \mathbf{60}$ Substitute 100 for l and 60 for w.

$ = 200 + 120$ Multiply.

$ = 320$ Add.

Natalie jogged 320 yd.

B Find the area of the triangle.

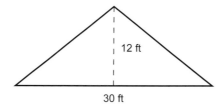

30 ft

12 ft

SOLUTION

Use the expression $\frac{1}{2}bh$, where b is the length of the base and h is the height of the triangle, to find the area. Evaluate $\frac{1}{2}bh$ when $b = 30$ and $h = 12$.

$\frac{1}{2}bh = \frac{1}{2} \cdot \mathbf{30} \cdot \mathbf{12}$ Substitute 30 for b and 12 for h.

$\phantom{\frac{1}{2}bh} = 15 \cdot 12$ Multiply from left to right.

$\phantom{\frac{1}{2}bh} = 180$ Multiply.

The area of the triangle is 180 ft^2.

C Find the number of miles the Perez family traveled if they drove nonstop for 2.5 h at a rate of 60 mph.

SOLUTION

Use the expression rt, where r is the rate of travel in miles per hour and t is the number of hours traveled, to find the number of miles the vehicle traveled. Evaluate rt when $r = 60$ and $t = 2.5$.

$rt = \mathbf{60 \cdot 2.5}$ Substitute 60 for r and 2.5 for t.

$ = 150$ Multiply.

The Perez family traveled 150 mi. ■

Translating Words into Expressions

To solve problems, you sometimes need to translate word phrases into variable expressions.

You can use the table to help determine what operation is indicated by a particular word phrase.

Matching Words and Phrases to Operations			
Addition	**Subtraction**	**Multiplication**	**Division**
plus	minus	times	quotient
more than	less than	product	separate into
increased by	decreased by	of	equal groups
sum	difference	combine	
total	shorter	equal	
longer	younger	groups	
older			

Think carefully when you translate. The phrases in the table do not automatically indicate particular operations. For example, *two is less than six* is written $2 < 6$; there is no subtraction involved.

Translating Word Phrases into Variable Expressions

EXAMPLE 1

Translate the word phrase into a variable expression.

A the sum of 16 and a number

SOLUTION

Possible variable expression:

$16 + n$ The word *sum* indicates addition. Use any letter for the variable.

B 6 less than twice a number

SOLUTION

Possible variable expression:

$2x - 6$ To represent 6 *less than* a quantity, you need to subtract 6 *from* that quantity. In this case, the quantity is twice a number, or 2 times a number.

C 20 students separated into equal groups

SOLUTION

Possible variable expression:

$\frac{20}{n}$ or $20 \div n$ You do not know how many equal groups, so use a variable for the number of equal groups. Use division to separate into equal groups.

> ▶ **Think About It** Order matters in subtraction and division. In Example 1B, $6 - 2x$ is incorrect. In Example 1C, $\frac{n}{20}$ and $n \div 20$ are incorrect.

D the number of seconds in m minutes

SOLUTION

Possible variable expression:

$60m$ You need to combine m "groups" of seconds with 60 in each group. Use multiplication to combine equal groups. ▪

> ▶ **Think About It** In Examples 1A, B, and C, the answers are given as possible expressions because they could contain different variables.

Translating Variable Expressions into Word Phrases

You can write a word phrase for a variable expression in more than one way.

Translate the variable expression into a word phrase.

A $m - 8$

SOLUTION
Possible answers include:

the difference of m and 8
8 less than m
m minus 8

B $bc + 2$

SOLUTION
Possible answers include:

the product of b and c, increased by 2
2 more than the product of b and c

C $b \cdot (c + 2)$

SOLUTION
Possible answers include:

the product of b and the sum of c and 2
b times 2 more than c
b times the quantity c plus 2 ▪

▶ **Think About It** Notice that the parentheses in Example 2C form an expression whose meaning is different from the expression in Example 2B.

Translating Variable Expressions into Real-World Problems

You can write real-world problems represented by a variable expression in more than one way.

EXAMPLE 3

Translate the variable expression into a real-world problem.

A $7 - y$

SOLUTION

Possible answers include:

Frank bought 7 bananas, but then ate some for breakfast. How many does he have left?

Bart ran 7 mi on Monday and y miles on Tuesday. How much farther did he run on Monday?

B $2g + 3$

SOLUTION

Possible answers include:

There are 2 cartons of eggs and 3 more eggs on the table. Each carton has the same number of eggs. How many eggs are there in all?

Jenna has 3 baseball cards. She buys 2 more packs of cards. Each pack has the same number of cards. How many cards does she have in all?

C $\dfrac{2h}{5}$

SOLUTION

Possible answers include:

Paul made 2 quiches. He cut them into slices. If 5 people share them, how many slices does each person get?

There are 2 karate classes. Each class has the same number of students. The students are divided among 5 buses. How many students should go on each bus? ■

Application: Age

EXAMPLE 4

A Sam's mom is 2 years older than 5 times Sam's age. Write a variable expression to represent the age of Sam's mom.

SOLUTION
Possible variable expression:

$5s + 2$ Let s represent Sam's age. The word *times* indicates multiplication. To represent 2 years older, add 2.

> ▶ **Remember** Expressions show relationships between different entities.

B The ages of three sisters are consecutive odd whole numbers. Write a variable expression to represent the age of the oldest sister if the age of the youngest sister is y.

> ▶ **Remember** Whole numbers are the numbers 0, 1, 2, 3, ...

SOLUTION
Consecutive whole numbers, such as 5 and 6, have no whole numbers between them. Consecutive odd whole numbers, such as 5 and 7, have no odd whole numbers between them.

Notice that to get from an odd whole number to the next consecutive odd whole number, you add 2. Therefore, the ages of the sisters are y, $y + 2$, and $y + 4$.

The variable expression for the age of the oldest sister is $y + 4$. ▪

Translating Mixed Operations

When translating an everyday situation into a math expression, you might need two or more operations.

> **Remember** Order of operations, when no exponents are used:
> 1. Operate inside parentheses.
> 2. Multiply and divide from left to right.
> 3. Add and subtract from left to right.

Translating Word Phrases into Expressions

Look for clues to help you decide which operations to use. Then identify variables for unknown quantities. Put the operations in the correct order in the expression. Use parentheses to show operations to be performed first.

EXAMPLE 1

Translate the phrase into a math expression.

A five less than the quotient of eight and four

SOLUTION
The words *less than* indicate subtraction and the word *quotient* indicates division.

The wording of the problem indicates that $8 \div 4$ should be calculated first. In the order of operations, division is performed before subtraction, so the expression doesn't need parentheses.

$$8 \div 4 - 5$$

B six times the sum of seven and a number

SOLUTION

The word *times* indicates multiplication and the word *sum* indicates addition.

Let n represent the number.

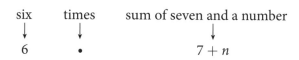

Use parentheses so that the sum is calculated before the product.

$$6 \cdot (7 + n) \blacksquare$$

EXAMPLE 2

Valerie has one climbing rope that is 150 ft long. She has some other ropes that are each 300 ft long. Write an expression that shows the total length of Valerie's climbing ropes.

SOLUTION

The word *each* indicates multiplication and the word *total* indicates addition.

Let r represent the number of ropes that are 300 ft long.

first rope	total	length of other ropes
↓	↓	↓
150	+	$r \cdot 300$

$$150 + 300r$$

Valene has $150 + 300r$ feet of climbing ropes in all. $\blacksquare$

Writing Word Phrases for Expressions

When writing a word phrase to represent a math expression with more than one operation, keep the order of operations in mind. Look for parentheses to tell you what operation to perform first. Choose words to represent the operations in the order that they should be performed.

EXAMPLE 3

Write a situation for the math expression.

A $6n - 4$

SOLUTION
The situation should represent subtracting 4 from the product of 6 and n.

Possible situation:
Michael buys some 6 packs of bottled water and gives away 4 bottles.

B $(18 + 32) \div p$

SOLUTION
The parentheses indicate that the sum $18 + 32$ is divided by p.

Possible situation:
Carlos has 18 pennies and 32 nickels. He divides the coins into equal piles. ■

Variable Expressions

Expressions can contain numbers, variables, and operation symbols. A numerical expression consists of numbers and one or more operations.

A variable is a symbol that represents a value. In most cases, variables are letters, such as x, y, a, and n. Most variables are lowercase and italicized.

A variable expression consists of one or more variables and one or more operations; it may also contain numbers.

Numerical expressions do not contain variables. Variable expressions do.

Numerical expressions	Variable expressions
$8 - 6 \cdot (3 + 1)$	$8 - 6 \cdot (a + b)$
$\dfrac{25}{8 - 3}$	$\dfrac{x}{y - z}$

A numerical expression has only one value. But a variable expression can have different values, depending on the values that are **substituted** for its variables.

▶ **Think About It** *Vary* means "change." Thus, when a variable changes its value, the value of the expression changes, too.

Evaluating Expressions

To **evaluate a variable expression**, replace all the variables in the expression with numbers and simplify. Remember to use the order of operations when simplifying.

When working with variable expressions, there are a few ways to show multiplication. You may be used to using the multiplication $\times$, but in algebra, you will most often see a raised dot. Also, you can show multiplication by putting a number right next to a variable. For instance, $6a$ is the same as $6 \cdot a$ and $6 \times a$.

> **Remember** Multiplication can be shown in different ways. All of the following mean six times the quantity three plus one.
>
> $$6(3+1) \qquad 6 \cdot (3+1) \qquad 6 \times (3+1)$$

EXAMPLE 1

A Evaluate $7n + 5$ when $n = 8$.

SOLUTION

$$7\boldsymbol{n} + 5 = 7 \cdot \boldsymbol{8} + 5 \qquad \text{Substitute 8 for } n.$$
$$= 56 + 5 \qquad \text{Multiply.}$$
$$= 61 \qquad \text{Add.}$$

B Evaluate $x - y + 2$ when $x = 11$ and $y = 3$.

SOLUTION

$$\boldsymbol{x} - \boldsymbol{y} + 2 = \boldsymbol{11} - \boldsymbol{3} + 2 \qquad \text{Substitute 11 for } x \text{ and 3 for } y.$$
$$= 8 + 2 \qquad \text{Subtract.}$$
$$= 10 \qquad \text{Add.}$$

C Evaluate $\dfrac{c - 5d}{10 \cdot (2d + 1)}$ when $c = 200$ and $d = 4$.

SOLUTION

$$\frac{\boldsymbol{c} - 5\boldsymbol{d}}{10 \cdot (2\boldsymbol{d} + 1)} = \frac{\boldsymbol{200} - 5 \cdot \boldsymbol{4}}{10 \cdot (2 \cdot \boldsymbol{4} + 1)} \qquad \text{Substitute 200 for } c \text{ and 4 for } d.$$

$$= \frac{200 - 20}{10 \cdot (9)} \qquad \text{Simplify the numerator and denominator separately.}$$

$$= \frac{180}{90}$$

$$= 2 \qquad \text{Divide.} \ \blacksquare$$

Application: Temperature

EXAMPLE 2

To approximate the temperature in degrees Celsius after an increase in altitude of f feet, you can use the expression $b - 2 \cdot \dfrac{f}{1000}$, where b is the beginning temperature. A hiker climbs 4000 ft to a summit from a parking lot, where it is 35°C. Approximate the temperature at the summit.

SOLUTION

$$b - 2 \cdot \frac{f}{1000} = 35 - 2 \cdot \frac{4000}{1000} \qquad \text{Substitute 35 for } b \text{ and 4000 for } f.$$

$$= 35 - 2 \cdot 4 \qquad \text{Divide.}$$

$$= 35 - 8 \qquad \text{Multiply.}$$

$$= 27 \qquad \text{Subtract.}$$

The temperature at the summit is about 27°C. ▪

Application: Sports

EXAMPLE 3

The distance around a rectangle is its perimeter and is given by the expression $2l + 2w$, where l represents length and w represents width. Find the perimeter of a soccer field that is 100 yd long and 60 yd wide.

SOLUTION

$$2l + 2w = 2 \cdot 100 + 2 \cdot 60 \qquad \text{Substitute 100 for } l \text{ and 60 for } w.$$

$$= 200 + 120 \qquad \text{Multiply.}$$

$$= 320 \qquad \text{Add.}$$

The perimeter of the soccer field is 320 yd. ▪

> ▶ **Think About It** Variables are often the first letters in the words they represent, such as *l* for length and *w* for width.

Equations and Inequalities

Topic List

Solving a tough problem can seem like climbing a mountain. Climbers know that to scale a mountain, you need a solid strategy and the correct tools, but you also need to do the little things right.

Comparing Expressions

The symbols for comparing expressions are $=$, $\neq$, $<$, $>$, $\leq$, and $\geq$.

You can use a number sentence to compare expressions.

Definitions

An **equation** is a number sentence indicating that two expressions have the same value. An equation is formed by placing an equals sign ($=$) between two expressions. For example, the equation $4 + 6 = 10$ indicates that $4 + 6$ and 10 have the same value.

An **inequality** is a number sentence formed by placing an inequality symbol ($\neq$, $<$, $>$, $\leq$, $\geq$) between two expressions. For example, $5 \neq 8$, $6 > 1 + 3$, and $6 - 5 < 2$.

Comparing Expressions

EXAMPLE 1

Use $<$, $=$, or $>$ to compare the expressions.

A $5 \bullet 2 + 7 \;\blacksquare\; 5 \bullet (2 + 7)$

SOLUTION
Simplify each expression. Then insert the correct symbol.

$$5 \bullet 2 + 7 \;\blacksquare\; 5 \bullet (2 + 7)$$
$$10 + 7 \;\blacksquare\; 5 \bullet 9$$
$$17 < 45$$

> **Remember** Order of operations, when no exponents are used:
> 1. Operate inside parentheses.
> 2. Multiply and divide from left to right.
> 3. Add and subtract from left to right.

B $\dfrac{10 - 6 + 14}{6}$  $5 \cdot 6 \div 10$

SOLUTION

Simplify each expression. Then insert the correct symbol.

$$\frac{10 - 6 + 14}{6} \;\blacksquare\; 5 \cdot 6 \div 10$$

$$\frac{18}{6} \;\blacksquare\; 30 \div 10$$

$$3 = 3 \;\blacksquare$$

Open Sentences and Solutions

Definition
An **open sentence** is an equation or inequality that contains one or more variables. For example, $x + 3 = 5$, $x - 1 > 4$, and $F = 1.8C + 32$.

An open sentence can be either true or false, depending on what values are substituted for the variables. A **solution** of an open sentence with one variable is a value that makes the sentence true. The solution of the equation $x + 3 = 5$ is 2. One solution of the inequality $x - 1 > 4$ is 6, and there are many more solutions.

You will see two more inequality symbols in open sentences. The less-than-or-equal-to symbol ($\leq$) indicates that one quantity is no more than the other. The greater-than-or-equal-to symbol ($\geq$) indicates that one quantity is no less than the other.

EXAMPLE 2

Determine whether the given value is a solution of the open sentence.

A $5x - 4 = 2; x = 2$

SOLUTION

Substitute 2 for x and simplify. Then decide if the sentence is true.

$$5x - 4 = 2$$

$$5 \cdot 2 - 4 \stackrel{?}{=} 2 \qquad \text{Substitute 2 for } x.$$

$$10 - 4 \stackrel{?}{=} 2 \qquad \text{Multiply.}$$

$$6 \neq 2 \qquad \text{Subtract.}$$

The sentence is not true when $x = 2$, so 2 is not a solution.

B $36 - a \cdot (a + 5); a = 4$

SOLUTION

Substitute 4 for a and simplify. Then decide if the sentence is true.

$$36 = a \cdot (a + 5)$$

$$36 \stackrel{?}{=} 4 \cdot (4 + 5) \qquad \text{Substitute 4 for } a.$$

$$36 \stackrel{?}{=} 4 \cdot 9 \qquad \text{Add inside the parentheses.}$$

$$36 = 36 \checkmark \qquad \text{Multiply.}$$

The sentence is true when $a = 4$, so 4 is a solution.

C $y \leq 2x + 5; x = 3 \text{ and } y = 11$

SOLUTION

Substitute 3 for x and 11 for y and simplify. Then decide if the sentence is true.

$$y \leq 2x + 5$$

$$11 \stackrel{?}{\leq} 2 \cdot 3 + 5 \qquad \text{Substitute 3 for } x \text{ and 11 for } y.$$

$$11 \stackrel{?}{\leq} 6 + 5 \qquad \text{Multiply.}$$

$$11 \leq 11 \checkmark \qquad \text{Add.}$$

The sentence is true when $x = 3$ and $y = 11$. ∎

Using Formulas to Compare Expressions

To compare expressions using formulas, substitute given values into the formulas and evaluate the expressions.

EXAMPLE 3

Compare the area of a rectangle with length 4 ft and width 3 ft to the area of a rectangle with length 6 ft and width 2 ft.

SOLUTION

Substitute the given values into to the formula for the area of a rectangle with length l and width w, $A = lw$.

First rectangle: Second rectangle:

First	Second	
$A = lw$	$A = lw$	Formula for area of a rectangle
$= 4 \cdot 3$	$= 6 \cdot 2$	Substitute given values.
$= 12$	$= 12$	Multiply.
	$12 = 12 \checkmark$	Compare.

The areas of the two rectangles are equal. ▪

EXAMPLE 4

Jane traveled for 3 h at a constant speed of 50 mph. John traveled for 2 h at a constant speed of 60 mph. Who traveled the greater distance?

SOLUTION

Substitute the given values into the formula for distance, $d = rt$, where r is the rate of speed and t is the time traveled.

Jane: John:

Jane	John	
$d = rt$	$d = rt$	Formula for distance
$= 50 \cdot 3$	$= 60 \cdot 2$	Substitute given values.
$= 150$	$= 120$	Multiply.
	$150 > 120$	Compare.

Jane traveled the greater distance. ▪

Replacement Sets

A replacement set for an open sentence is a set of values that are possible solutions. That is, the values in a replacement set are tested to see if they are solutions.

A **solution** of an open sentence with one variable is a value of the variable that makes the sentence a true statement.

A **set** is a collection of objects. Each member of a set is an **element** of the set. The elements of a set are enclosed in braces, so the set containing the elements 9, 12, and 15 is written as $\{9, 12, 15\}$. The symbol $\in$ is used to show that a value is an element of a set.

▶ **Think About It**
NOTATION The symbol $\in$ means "is an element of."
For example, $3 \in \{1, 3, 5, 7\}$.

Definitions

A **replacement set** for an open sentence is a set of values that are allowable as solutions of the open sentence.

A **solution set** for an open sentence is a set of values that are solutions of the open sentence with the given replacement set.

A solution set can have any number of values. An open sentence can have zero, one, or many solutions, depending on the type of open sentence.

Finding Solutions of Open Sentences from a Replacement Set

EXAMPLE 1

Identify the solution set of the open sentence using the given replacement set.

A $2x + 1 = 5$; replacement set $\{0, 1, 2\}$

SOLUTION

Substitute each replacement set value for x.

$$2x + 1 = 5 \qquad\qquad 2x + 1 = 5 \qquad\qquad 2x + 1 = 5$$
$$2 \cdot 0 + 1 \overset{?}{=} 5 \qquad 2 \cdot 1 + 1 \overset{?}{=} 5 \qquad 2 \cdot 2 + 1 \overset{?}{=} 5$$
$$0 + 1 \overset{?}{=} 5 \qquad\quad 2 + 1 \overset{?}{=} 5 \qquad\quad 4 + 1 \overset{?}{=} 5$$
$$1 \neq 5 \qquad\qquad 3 \neq 5 \qquad\qquad 5 = 5 \checkmark$$

The only solution is 2. The solution set is $\{2\}$.

B $x + 3 < 10$; replacement set $\{5, 6, 7, 8\}$

SOLUTION

Substitute each replacement set value for x.

$$x + 3 < 10 \qquad x + 3 < 10 \qquad x + 3 < 10 \qquad x + 3 < 10$$
$$5 + 3 \overset{?}{<} 10 \qquad 6 + 3 \overset{?}{<} 10 \qquad 7 + 3 \overset{?}{<} 10 \qquad 8 + 3 \overset{?}{<} 10$$
$$8 < 10 \checkmark \qquad\quad 9 < 10 \checkmark \qquad\quad 10 \not< 10 \qquad\quad 11 \not< 10$$

Using the given replacement set, the solutions are 5 and 6. The solution set is $\{5, 6\}$. ∎

Finding Solutions of an Equation with the Variable on Both Sides

If the variable occurs more than once in an equation, remember to substitute a possible solution for each occurrence of the variable.

EXAMPLE 2

Identify the solution set, if any, using the given replacement set.

A $x + 6 = 14 - x$; replacement set $\{4, 8, 10\}$

SOLUTION

Substitute each replacement set value for x.

$$x + 6 = 14 - x \qquad\qquad x + 6 = 14 - x \qquad\qquad x + 6 = 14 - x$$
$$4 + 6 \overset{?}{=} 14 - 4 \qquad\qquad 8 + 6 \overset{?}{=} 14 - 8 \qquad\qquad 10 + 6 \overset{?}{=} 14 - 10$$
$$10 \overset{?}{=} 10 \qquad\qquad\qquad 14 \overset{?}{=} 6 \qquad\qquad\qquad 16 \overset{?}{=} 4$$
$$10 = 10 \checkmark \qquad\qquad\qquad 14 \neq 6 \qquad\qquad\qquad 16 \neq 4$$

The only solution is 4. The solution set is $\{4\}$.

B $x + 11 = 15 + x$; replacement set $\{4, 6, 26\}$

SOLUTION

Substitute each replacement set value for x.

$$x + 11 = 15 + x \qquad\qquad x + 11 = 15 + x \qquad\qquad x + 11 = 15 + x$$
$$4 + 11 \overset{?}{=} 15 + 4 \qquad\qquad 6 + 11 \overset{?}{=} 15 + 6 \qquad\qquad 26 + 11 \overset{?}{=} 15 + 26$$
$$15 \overset{?}{=} 19 \qquad\qquad\qquad 17 \overset{?}{=} 21 \qquad\qquad\qquad 37 \overset{?}{=} 41$$
$$15 \neq 19 \qquad\qquad\qquad 17 \neq 21 \qquad\qquad\qquad 37 \neq 41$$

No member of the replacement set is a solution. No member of the replacement set makes the open sentence true. The solution set is a set with no members, called the **empty set** (written as $\varnothing$). ▪

> ▶ **Think About It**
>
> **NOTATION** The equation in Example 2B has no solution, even using the set of all numbers as the replacement set. The symbols $\{\ \}$ or $\varnothing$ mean null or empty set.

Application: Temperature

EXAMPLE 3

The formula $F = 1.8C + 32$ is used to convert degrees Celsius (°C) to degrees Fahrenheit (°F). For 41°F, the equation is $41 = 1.8C + 32$. Find the temperature in degrees Celsius that corresponds to 41°F by using the replacement set $\{3, 4, 5\}$ for C.

SOLUTION

Substitute each replacement set value for C.

$41 = 1.8C + 32$　　　　$41 = 1.8C + 32$　　　　$41 = 1.8C + 32$

$41 \overset{?}{=} 1.8 \cdot \mathbf{3} + 32$　　$41 \overset{?}{=} 1.8 \cdot \mathbf{4} + 32$　　$41 \overset{?}{=} 1.8 \cdot \mathbf{5} + 32$

$41 \overset{?}{=} 5.4 + 32$　　　$41 \overset{?}{=} 7.2 + 32$　　　$41 \overset{?}{=} 9.0 + 32$

$41 \overset{?}{=} 37.4$　　　　$41 \overset{?}{=} 39.2$　　　　$41 \overset{?}{=} 41$

$41 \neq 37.4$　　　　　$41 \neq 39.2$　　　　　$41 = 41$ ✓

So 5°C corresponds to 41°F. ▪

▶ **Remember** Algebraic equations can capture key relationships among quantities in the world.

Translating Words into Equations

Just as you can translate a phrase into an expression, you can translate a complete sentence into an equation.

If a sentence describes two equal quantities, it can be translated into an equation. The word *is* should usually be translated into an equals sign.

▶ **Remember** Equations express relationships between different entities.

Translating Sentences into Equations

EXAMPLE 1

Translate the sentence into an equation.

A Twenty-five times a number is 150.

SOLUTION

Twenty-five times **a number**   is   150.

$$25 \cdot n = 150$$

$$25n = 150$$

The word *times* indicates multiplication and the word *is* indicates an equals sign.

B Fourteen is the sum of a number and 6.

SOLUTION

Fourteen	is	the sum of **a number** and **6.**
14	=	$n + 6$

The word *sum* indicates addition and the word *is* indicates an equals sign.

C Two less than 5 times a number is 7.

SOLUTION

$5n$ Translate *5 times a number.*

$5n - 2$ Translate *two less than 5 times a number.*

$5n - 2 = 7$ Write the equation. ■

Translating Equations into Sentences

EXAMPLE 2

Translate the equation into a sentence.

A $2 + (d + 3) = 10$

SOLUTION
Possible answer:
Two increased by the sum of a number and 3 is 10.

B $2a = \dfrac{8}{a}$

SOLUTION
Possible answer:
Twice a number is the quotient of 8 and the number. ■

Writing Equations and Identifying Solutions

EXAMPLE 3

Translate the sentence into an equation. Then identify the solution, using the given replacement set.

A The product of 6 and a number is 42. Replacement set: $\{7, 36, 48\}$

SOLUTION

The product of 6 and a number is 42.

$6s$	$= 42$	The word *product* indicates multiplication.
		Write an equation.
$6 \cdot 7$	$= 42$	Substitute 7 for s.
42	$= 42$	When $s = 7$, the equation is true.

The solution is $s = 7$.

▶ **Remember** Substitute each value in the replacement set for the variable. Then decide which value makes the equation true.

B Nine is 3 more than twice a number. Replacement set: $\{2, 3, 6\}$

SOLUTION

Nine is 3 more than twice a number.

9	$= 2n + 3$	The phrase *more than* indicates addition.
		Write an equation.
9	$= 2 \cdot 3 + 3$	Substitute 3 for n.
9	$= 9$	When $n = 3$, the equation is true.

The solution is $n = 3$. ∎

Application: Writing Formulas

A formula is an equation that describes a relationship among quantities.

> ▶ **Think About It** Distance and time are quantities. Rate is a ratio of those quantities. For example, if $d = 40$ mi and $t = 2$ h, then
>
> $$r = \frac{d}{t} = \frac{40 \text{ mi}}{2 \text{ h}} = \frac{20 \text{ mi}}{1 \text{ h}} = 20 \text{ mph.}$$

EXAMPLE 4

Write a formula that describes the relationship.

A If an object travels at a constant rate, the distance the object travels is the product of its rate and the amount of time it travels.

SOLUTION

Let d represent distance, r represent rate, and t represent time.

Distance is the product of rate and time.	Write a brief sentence.
$d = rt$	Translate the sentence into an equation.

B The perimeter of a triangle is the sum of the lengths of its sides.

SOLUTION

Let P represent perimeter. Let a, b, and c represent the lengths of the sides.

Perimeter is the sum of the lengths of the sides.	Write a brief sentence.
$P = a + b + c$	Translate the sentence into an equation. ▪

Addition and Subtraction Equations

An addition equation can represent many problem situations.

Solving Equations

Definitions

A **solution** of an equation with one variable is a value of the variable that makes the equation a true statement.

Equivalent equations are equations with the exact same solutions.

▶ **Remember** The quantities on both sides of an equation are equal.

Strategy: Guess-and-Test

One strategy you can use to solve addition equations is guess-and-test. With this method, guess a value for the variable that you think will make the equation true, and then test your guess. If your guess is wrong, make another guess using what you learned from your previous guesses.

EXAMPLE 1

The perimeter of the figure is 14 m. What is the length of the side labeled x?

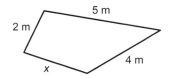

SOLUTION

The sum of the lengths of the sides is 14 m. Write an equation. Simplify.

$$x + 2 + 5 + 4 = 14$$
$$x + 11 = 14$$

Use guess-and-test.
Test $x = 2$: $\mathbf{2} + 11 \stackrel{?}{=} 14$
$$13 \neq 14$$

The equation is not true. Try a greater value.
Test $x = 3$: $\mathbf{3} + 11 \stackrel{?}{=} 14$
$$14 = 14 \checkmark$$

Side x is 3 m long. ■

Strategy: Using Properties

You'll find it easier to solve an equation if you can get the variable alone on one side of the equation. Properties can help you do that.

Addition and Subtraction Properties of Equality

The **addition and subtraction properties of equality** state that if you add or subtract the same number from both sides of an equation, the sides remain equal.

$$\text{If } a = b, \text{ then } a + c = b + c$$
$$\text{and } a - c = b - c.$$

Identity Property of Addition

The **identity property of addition** states that adding zero to a number gives a sum identical to that number.

$$a + 0 = a$$

▶ **Think About It** An equation is like a set of scales. To keep scales in balance, you must add equal weights to each side. Whatever you do to one side of the equation, you also must do to the other side to keep the sides equal.

EXAMPLE 2

Solve for y.

$$y - 7 = 19$$

SOLUTION

▶ **Remember** Addition and subtraction are inverse operations. They undo each other. So to "undo" the subtraction of 7, you can add 7.

$$y - 7 = 19$$

$y - 7 + 7 = 19 + 7$ Add 7 to both sides.

$y + 0 = 26$ Simplify.

$y = 26$ Apply the identity property of addition.

CHECK

Replace y with 26 in the original equation. Then simplify and see if you have a true equation.

$y - 7 = 19$
$26 - 7 \overset{?}{=} 19$
$19 = 19 \checkmark$

Since the solution checks, you have a true equation. ■

EXAMPLE 3

Jaime's car can travel 500 km on a tank of gas. If she began with a full tank of gas and traveled 350 km, how much farther can she travel on that tank?

SOLUTION

Write an equation to represent the situation. Let d represent how much farther Jaime can travel.

$$d + 350 = 500 \qquad \text{Write an equation.}$$

$$d + 350 - \mathbf{350} = 500 - \mathbf{350} \qquad \text{Subtract 350 from both sides.}$$

$$d + 0 = 150 \qquad \text{Simplify.}$$

$$d = 150$$

Jaime can travel 150 km farther. ▪

Equations Involving Addition and Subtraction

To solve equations, you need to understand equivalent equations.

Equivalent equations are equations with the same solution or solutions. Related equations are equivalent, but you can also use properties of equality to create equivalent equations.

Properties of Equality

Property	Example
Addition Property of Equality If you add the same number to both sides of an equation, you obtain an equivalent equation.	
If $a = b$, then $a + c = b + c$ and $c + a = c + b$.	If $n = 3$, then $n + 2 = 3 + 2$. If $x - 4 = 9$, then $x - 4 + 4 = 9 + 4$.
Subtraction Property of Equality If you subtract the same number from both sides of an equation, you obtain an equivalent equation.	
If $a = b$, then $a - c = b - c$.	If $r = 7$, then $r - 5 = 7 - 5$. If $x + 3 = 12$, then $x + 3 - 3 = 12 - 3$.
Substitution Property of Equality A value or expression may replace an equal value or expression.	
If $a = b$, then either may replace the other in any expression.	If $x = 6$, then you can rewrite the expression $x - 10$ as $6 - 10$.

Solving Addition and Subtraction Equations

Addition and subtraction are **inverse operations**. To solve an equation, use inverse operations to obtain one or more simpler equations that are equivalent. When you obtain the simplest equivalent equation, you have the solution.

Solving Addition and Subtraction Equations

If a number is subtracted from a variable in an equation, you can add that same number to both sides of the equation to undo the subtraction.

If a number is added to a variable in an equation, you can subtract that same number from both sides of the equation to undo the addition.

EXAMPLE 1

Solve the equation. Check your answer.

A $x - 10 = 4$

SOLUTION

$$x - 10 = 4$$
$$x - 10 + 10 = 4 + 10 \qquad \text{To undo the subtraction, add 10 to both sides.}$$
$$x + 0 = 14 \qquad \text{Opposites sum to zero.}$$
$$x = 14$$

▶ **Think About It** You don't often see the step $x + 0 = 14$, but it's always implied.

CHECK

$$x - 10 = 4$$
$$14 - 10 \overset{?}{=} 4 \qquad \text{Substitute 14 for } x.$$
$$4 = 4 \checkmark$$

B $x + 5 = 10$

SOLUTION

$$x + 5 = 10$$

$$x + 5 - 5 = 10 - 5 \qquad \text{To undo the addition, subtract 5 from both sides.}$$

$$x = 5$$

CHECK

$$x + 5 = 10$$

$$5 + 5 \stackrel{?}{=} 10 \qquad \text{Substitute 5 for } x.$$

$$10 = 10 \checkmark \ \blacksquare$$

Solving Equations Involving Decimals

Use the same strategies that you use with integers to solve equations with decimals.

EXAMPLE 2

Solve.

A $x + 5.3 = 15$

SOLUTION

$$x + 5.3 = 15$$

$$x + 5.3 - 5.3 = 15 - 5.3 \qquad \text{Subtract 5.3 from both sides.}$$

$$x = 9.7$$

B $23 = d - 9.5$

SOLUTION

$23 = d - 9.5$

$23 + 9.5 = d - 9.5 + 9.5$ Add 9.5 to both sides.

$32.5 = d$ ■

Simplifying Before Solving

With some equations, it is easier to simplify one side of the equation before you perform an inverse operation.

EXAMPLE 3

Solve the equation.

$5.2 + x + 3.8 = 13$

SOLUTION

$5.2 + x + 3.8 = 13$

$x + 5.2 + 3.8 = 13$ Use the associative property to rearrange the addends.

$x + 9 = 13$ Add 5.2 and 3.8 to simplify the left side.

$x + 9 - 9 = 13 - 9$ Subtract 9 from both sides.

$x = 4$ ■

Application: Landscape Design

EXAMPLE 4

A landscaper has 20 m of border for a garden. She has planned the lengths of three sides, as shown in the diagram. What length is needed for the fourth side so that she can use the entire border?

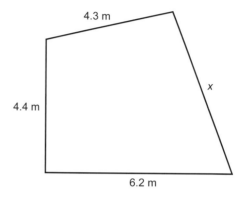

SOLUTION

$$6.2 + 4.4 + 4.3 + x = 20.0$$
$$14.9 + x = 20.0$$
$$14.9 + x - 14.9 = 20.0 - 14.9$$
$$x - 14.9 + 14.9 = 20.0 - 14.9$$
$$x = 5.1$$

The length of the fourth side should be 5.1 m. ■

Equations Involving Multiplication and Division

If you divide both sides of an equation by the same nonzero number, the equation will still be true. You can use the division property of equality to solve equations.

Using the Division Property of Equality to Solve Equations

You can use the division property of equality to find equivalent equations. The point of this sort of transformation is to find an equation that makes the solution easy to see.

Division Property of Equality

For a, b, and n (where $n \neq 0$),

If $\qquad a = b$

then $\quad \dfrac{a}{n} = \dfrac{b}{n}$

Example

If $\qquad 2x = 6$

then $\quad \dfrac{2x}{2} = \dfrac{6}{2}$

$\qquad\qquad x = 3$

All three of these are equivalent equations.

▶ **Remember** Equivalent equations have the same solution.

EXAMPLE 1

Solve.

A $5 \cdot r = 30$

SOLUTION

$5 \cdot r = 30$

$\dfrac{5 \cdot r}{5} = \dfrac{30}{5}$ Divide both sides of the equation by 5.

$1 \cdot r = 6$ Simplify.

$r = 6$ Use the identity property of multiplication.

> ▶ **Think About It** Check your answer by substituting 6 for r in the original equation. The result should be a true equation.
>
> $$5 \cdot r = 30$$
> $$5 \cdot (6) = 30$$
> $$30 = 30 \checkmark$$

B $2.1 = 7b$

SOLUTION

$2.1 = 7b$

$\dfrac{2.1}{7} = \dfrac{7b}{7}$ Divide both sides of the equation by 7.

$0.3 = 1 \cdot b$ Simplify.

$0.3 = b$ Use the identity property of multiplication. ▪

Using the Multiplication Property of Equality to Solve Equations

If you multiply both sides of an equation by the same number, the equation will still be true. You can use the multiplication property of equality to solve equations.

Multiplication Property of Equality

For a, b, and n,

If $\quad a = b$

then $\quad an = bn$

Example

If $\quad \dfrac{x}{5} = 3$

then $\quad \dfrac{x}{5} \cdot 5 = 3 \cdot 5$

$\qquad\qquad x = 15$

All three of these are equivalent equations.

EXAMPLE 2

Solve.

A $\dfrac{b}{3} = 10$

SOLUTION

$\dfrac{b}{3} = 10$

$\dfrac{b}{3} \cdot 3 = 10 \cdot 3 \qquad$ Multiply both sides of the equation by 3.

$b \cdot 1 = 30 \qquad$ Simplify.

$b = 30 \qquad$ Use the identity property of multiplication.

B $3 = \dfrac{w}{0.65}$

SOLUTION

$3 = \dfrac{w}{0.65}$

$3 \cdot 0.65 = \dfrac{w}{0.65} \cdot 0.65 \qquad$ Multiply both sides of the equation by 0.65.

$1.95 = w \cdot 1 \qquad$ Simplify.

$1.95 = w \qquad$ Use the identity property of multiplication. ▪

Using the Reciprocal to Solve an Equation

When the variable in an equation is multiplied by a fraction, multiply both sides by the reciprocal of the fraction to solve. Multiplying by the reciprocal is the same as dividing.

EXAMPLE 3

Solve.

$$\frac{2}{3}p = 6$$

SOLUTION

$$\frac{2}{3}p = 6$$

$$\frac{2}{3} \cdot \frac{3}{2} \cdot p = 6 \cdot \frac{3}{2} \qquad \text{Multiply both sides of the equation by } \frac{3}{2}.$$

$$1 \cdot p = 9 \qquad \text{Simplify. The product of reciprocals is 1.}$$

$$p = 9 \qquad \text{Use the identity property of multiplication.} \ \blacksquare$$

▶ **Remember** $6 \cdot \dfrac{3}{2} = \dfrac{6}{1} \cdot \dfrac{3}{2}$

$$= \dfrac{\overset{3}{\cancel{6}}}{1} \cdot \dfrac{3}{\underset{1}{\cancel{2}}}$$

$$= \dfrac{9}{1}$$

$$= 9$$

Application: Science

EXAMPLE 4

Scientists estimate the fish population in a lake every year. In 2008, the estimate was 22,500 fish. The estimate for 2008 was three times the estimate for 2005. What was the estimate for 2005?

SOLUTION

Use the words to write an equation. The unknown quantity is the estimate for 2005.

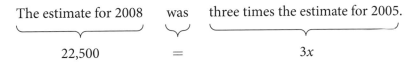

> **Think About It** When modeling a problem, the words *is* and *was* can often be translated to equals signs.

The estimate for 2008	was	three times the estimate for 2005.
22,500	$=$	$3x$

Solve the equation.

$$22{,}500 = 3x$$

$$\frac{22{,}500}{3} = \frac{3x}{3} \qquad \text{Divide both sides of the equation by 3.}$$

$$7500 = x \qquad \text{Simplify both sides of the equation.} \ \blacksquare$$

Inequalities

You can use inequality symbols to compare two expressions that are not equal.

Translating Sentences into Inequalities

EXAMPLE 1

Translate the sentence into an inequality.

> ▶ **Remember** An inequality is a number sentence that includes one of the symbols $<$, $>$, $\leq$, or $\geq$.

A Four plus one is greater than two minus one.

SOLUTION

Four plus one	is greater than	two minus one.
$4 + 1$	$>$	$2 - 1$

The inequality is $4 + 1 > 2 - 1$, or $5 > 1$.

B Seven and two-tenths minus three is less than two times three.

SOLUTION

Seven and two-tenths minus three	is less than	two times three.
$7.2 - 3$	$<$	$2 \cdot 3$

The inequality is $7.2 - 3 < 2 \cdot 3$, or $4.2 < 6$.

C Two times two is less than or equal to two squared.

> **SOLUTION**
>
> | Two times two | is less than or equal to | two squared. |
> |:---:|:---:|:---:|
> | $2 \cdot 2$ | $\leq$ | 2^2 |
>
> The inequality is $2 \cdot 2 \leq 2^2$, or $4 \leq 4$.

D More than 300 fans are expected to attend the game today.

> **SOLUTION**
>
> The number of fans attending the game is unknown, so use the variable x to represent number of fans.
>
> | number of fans | more than | 300 |
> |:---:|:---:|:---:|
> | x | $>$ | 300 |
>
> The inequality is $x > 300$.

E In the last 6 months, fewer than 125 homes were sold in the county.

> **SOLUTION**
>
> Use the variable x to represent the number of homes sold in the last 6 months.
>
> | number of homes | fewer than | 125 |
> |:---:|:---:|:---:|
> | x | $<$ | 125 |
>
> The inequality is $x < 125$. ■

Translating Inequalities into Sentences

Just as you can translate a sentence into an inequality, you can translate an inequality into a sentence.

EXAMPLE 2

Translate the inequality into a sentence.

A $x < 6$

SOLUTION
The inequality $x < 6$ translates to "x is **less than** six."

B $x \geq -10$

SOLUTION
The inequality $x \geq -10$ translates to "x is **greater than or equal to** negative ten."

C $x < 4.1$

SOLUTION
The inequality $x < 4.1$ translates to "x is **less than** four and one-tenth." ■

Determining the Truth of an Inequality

EXAMPLE 3

Determine whether the inequality is true or false.

A $8 > 5$

SOLUTION
Translate the inequality into a sentence and use your number sense to determine its truth.

$8 > 5 \leftrightarrow$ "Eight **is greater than** five."

Yes, eight is greater than five. This inequality is true.

B $2.7 < -6$

SOLUTION

$2.7 < -6 \leftrightarrow$ "Two and seven-tenths **is less than** negative six."

No positive number is less than a negative number. This inequality is false.

C $-3 \geq -3$

SOLUTION

$-3 \geq -3 \leftrightarrow$ "Negative three **is greater than or equal to** negative three."

Although negative three is not greater than negative three, the two numbers are equal to each other. This inequality is true. ■

Determining Whether a Given Value Is a Solution of an Inequality

Like equations, inequalities may contain variable terms. A **solution of an inequality** is a value of the variable that makes the equation true.

EXAMPLE 4

Determine whether $x = -5$ is a solution of $x \leq -9$.

SOLUTION

Substitute the value and determine the truth of the inequality.

$x \leq -9$

$-5 \overset{?}{\leq} -9$ Substitute -5 for x.

$-5 \nleq -9$ False. If necessary, use a number line to see that -5 is actually greater (farther right) than -9.

No, $x = -5$ is not a solution of the inequality $x \leq -9$. ■

Solutions to Inequalities

An equation, such as $x = 1$, has exactly one solution, or value of x, that makes the number sentence true. An inequality, such as $x > 1$, has many solutions that make it true—in this case, any value for x that is greater than the value of 1.

EXAMPLE 5

An inequality has more than one solution. List five possible solutions for the inequality.

A $x < -3$

▶ **Think About It** Draw a number line to help you. Place 0 in the middle, negative numbers to the left, and positive numbers to the right.

SOLUTION
The solutions to the inequality $x < -3$ are all numbers less than -3. All solutions must lie to the left of -3 on a number line. Five possible solutions are $-4, -4.5, -5, -10,$ and -15.

B $x \geq 12.4$

▶ **Think About It** Any number that is 12.4 or greater is part of the solution set.

SOLUTION
The solutions to the inequality $x \geq 12.4$ are all numbers greater than or equal to 12.4. All solutions must lie either directly at or to the right of 12.4 on a number line. Five possible solutions are 12.4, 12.5, 13, 20, and 100.

C $x < 0$

SOLUTION
The solutions to the inequality $x < 0$ are all numbers less than 0. All solutions must lie to the left of 0 on a number line. Five possible solutions are $-\frac{1}{2}, -2, -6, -12,$ and -100. ▪

EXAMPLE 6

Which of the following numbers are solutions to the inequality $x \geq -\frac{2}{3}$?

$$0, -\frac{5}{6}, \frac{2}{3}, 6, -\frac{1}{3}, -10, -1$$

SOLUTION

Choose numbers that are greater than or equal to $-\frac{2}{3}$. The solutions are $0, \frac{2}{3}, 6,$ and $-\frac{1}{3}.$ ∎

An inequality frequently has infinitely many solutions. For example, the solutions of $x \geq 2$ are all real numbers greater than or equal to 2, including 2, 2.001, 3, 3000, and 1,000,000, to name a few. You could never list all of the numbers greater than or equal to 2, but you can represent the solution set of $x \geq 2$ on a number line.

Definitions

The **graph of an inequality** is a display of all possible solutions of the inequality.

A **ray** is part of a line that starts at an endpoint and extends infinitely in one direction.

If you try to plot all of the real numbers greater than or equal to 2, the points cover all of the number line to the right of 2, creating a ray with endpoint 2. Because 2 is a solution to $x \geq 2$, it is shown as a closed circle.

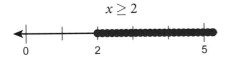 becomes

How would you graph $x > 2$? All the solutions of $x > 2$ are solutions of $x \geq 2$. The only difference between the solutions is the endpoint, since 2 is not greater than 2. Therefore, the graph of $x > 2$ is the same ray as the graph of $x \geq 2$, but the endpoint is an open circle to show that 2 is not a solution.

$$x > 2$$

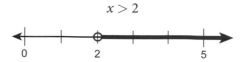

For "less than" inequalities, the ray points left.

$$x \leq 2 \qquad\qquad x < 2$$

Graphing a Simple Inequality

Graph the inequality on a number line.

> ▶ **Think About It** When the variable is isolated on the left side of an inequality, the inequality symbol mimics the direction of the ray. That is, $x \geq 2$ and $x > 2$ have right-facing rays: →. $x \leq 2$ and $x < 2$ have left-facing rays: ←.

A $x < -1$

SOLUTION

To graph $x < -1$, use a **left**-facing ray with an **open** circle at -1.

$$x < -1$$

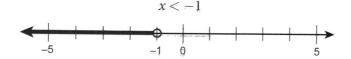

B $t \geq 3.5$

SOLUTION

To graph $t \geq 3.5$, use a **right**-facing ray with a **closed** circle at 3.5. The endpoint does not fall on a tick mark, so be sure to include a label.

$$t \geq 3.5$$

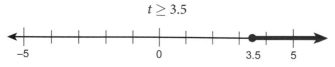

C $n > 0$

SOLUTION

To graph $n > 0$, use a **right**-facing ray with an **open** circle at 0.

$$n > 0$$

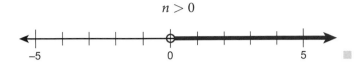

Graphing an Inequality with a Restricted Domain

Some inequalities have a restricted domain such as whole numbers or integers.

To graph an inequality with a restricted domain, first imagine the graph as if the domain were all real numbers. Then adjust the endpoint(s) and ray(s) or segment to represent the correct domain.

EXAMPLE 8

Graph $x \geq -1.25$ over the domain $x \in \mathbb{Z}$.

> **Remember** The symbol for real numbers is $\mathbb{R}$, integers is $\mathbb{Z}$, whole numbers is $\mathbb{W}$, and natural numbers is $\mathbb{N}$.

SOLUTION

First imagine the graph of $x \geq -1.25$ for all real numbers.

Now adjust the graph for the restricted domain of integers.

$$x \geq -1.25, x \in \mathbb{Z}$$

Move the endpoint to −1, the nearest integer within the ray.

Replace the ray with points on each integer.

Use an ellipsis (...) instead of an arrow to show that the pattern continues.

Working with Improper Fractions and Mixed Numbers

Sometimes it is easier to work with a value as a mixed number, but other times it is better to work with an equivalent improper fraction.

If you keep in mind that a mixed number is the sum of a whole number and a fraction, you can express the mixed number as an improper fraction.

To convert a mixed number to an improper fraction, just use common denominators to add the whole part of the mixed number to the fraction part. If you do the same thing with variables as you work with a specific example, you can see how the general strategy works.

With numbers:

$$5\frac{1}{2} = 5 + \frac{1}{2}$$

With variables:

$$x\frac{a}{b} = x + \frac{a}{b}$$

$$= \frac{5}{1} + \frac{1}{2} \qquad\qquad = \frac{x}{1} + \frac{a}{b} \qquad\qquad \text{Write the whole as a fraction with denominator 1.}$$

$$= \frac{5}{1} \cdot \frac{2}{2} + \frac{1}{2} \qquad\qquad = \frac{x}{1} \cdot \frac{b}{b} + \frac{a}{b} \qquad\qquad \text{Multiply to get common denominators.}$$

$$= \frac{5 \cdot 2}{1 \cdot 2} + \frac{1}{2} \qquad\qquad = \frac{x \cdot b}{1 \cdot b} + \frac{a}{b} \qquad\qquad \text{Simplify.}$$

$$= \frac{5 \cdot 2}{2} + \frac{1}{2} \qquad\qquad = \frac{x \cdot b}{b} + \frac{a}{b} \qquad\qquad \text{Simplify.}$$

$$= \frac{5 \cdot 2 + 1}{2} \qquad\qquad = \frac{x \cdot b + a}{b} \qquad\qquad \text{Add fractions.}$$

$$= \frac{10 + 1}{2} = \frac{11}{2} \qquad\qquad\qquad\qquad \text{Simplify the number problem.}$$

> ▶ **Think About It** The number $5\frac{1}{2}$ is not the same as $5 \cdot \frac{1}{2}$. It is the same as $5 + \frac{1}{2}$.

Converting Mixed Numbers to Improper Fractions

EXAMPLE 1

Convert the mixed number to an improper fraction.

$$2\frac{3}{5}$$

SOLUTION

$$2\frac{3}{5} = \frac{2 \cdot 5 + 3}{5}$$ Multiply the whole part by the denominator. Add the result to the numerator.

$$= \frac{13}{5}$$ Simplify. ■

Adding and Subtracting Mixed Numbers

A mixed number has an integer part and a fraction part.

$$3 \text{ is the integer part} \longrightarrow 3\frac{2}{5} \longleftarrow \frac{2}{5} \text{ is the fraction part}$$

Adding and Subtracting with Mixed Numbers

Method 1 Add or subtract the integer parts and fraction parts separately. Simplify if possible.

Method 2 Write integers and mixed numbers as improper fractions. Add or subtract the fractions. Simplify if possible.

EXAMPLE 2

Find the value of the expression. Write the answer in simplest form.

A $2\frac{3}{4} + 3\frac{1}{12}$

SOLUTION
Use Method 1.

$$2\frac{3}{4} = 2\frac{9}{12}$$
Write $\frac{3}{4}$ as the equivalent fraction $\frac{9}{12}$.

$$+\,3\frac{1}{12} = 3\frac{1}{12}$$
Add the integer parts: $2 + 3 = 5$.
Add the fraction parts: $\frac{9}{12} + \frac{1}{12} = \frac{10}{12}$.

$$5\frac{10}{12} = 5\frac{5}{6}$$
Simplify.

B $\frac{1}{8} + 1\frac{3}{10}$

SOLUTION
Use Method 2.

$$\frac{1}{8} + 1\frac{3}{10} = \frac{1}{8} + \frac{13}{10}$$
Write the mixed number as an improper fraction.

$$= \frac{5}{40} + \frac{52}{40}$$
Write each fraction as an equivalent fraction, using the least common denominator 40.

$$= \frac{57}{40}$$
Add the fractions.

$$= 1\frac{17}{40}$$
Simplify by writing the improper fraction as a mixed number.

C $4 - 2\frac{2}{5} + \frac{1}{2}$

SOLUTION

Use Method 2.

$4 - 2\dfrac{2}{5} + \dfrac{1}{2} = \dfrac{4}{1} - \dfrac{12}{5} + \dfrac{1}{2}$ 　　Write the integer and mixed number as improper fractions.

$= \dfrac{40}{10} - \dfrac{24}{10} + \dfrac{5}{10}$ 　　Write each fraction as an equivalent fraction, using the least common denominator 10.

$= \dfrac{40 - 24 + 5}{10}$

$= \dfrac{21}{10}$ 　　Subtract and add to simplify the expression in the numerator.

$= 2\dfrac{1}{10}$ 　　Write the improper fraction as a mixed number to simplify. ■

Application: Carpentry

EXAMPLE 3

A carpenter cuts a board $10\frac{3}{4}$ in. long from a board $33\frac{1}{4}$ in. long.

The saw cut is $\frac{1}{8}$ in. wide. What is the length of the remaining piece?

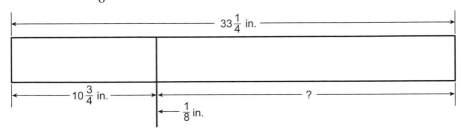

SOLUTION

Subtract $10\frac{3}{4}$ and $\frac{1}{8}$ from $33\frac{1}{4}$. Use Method 2.

$$33\frac{1}{4} - 10\frac{3}{4} - \frac{1}{8} = \frac{133}{4} - \frac{43}{4} - \frac{1}{8}$$

$$= \frac{266}{8} - \frac{86}{8} - \frac{1}{8}$$

$$= \frac{179}{8}$$

$$= 22\frac{3}{8}$$

The remaining piece is $22\frac{3}{8}$ in. long. ∎

▶ **Think About It** The expression $33\frac{1}{4} - \left(10\frac{3}{4} + \frac{1}{8}\right)$ can be used in this application. Find the sum $10\frac{3}{4} + \frac{1}{8}$ and then subtract that result from $33\frac{1}{4}$.

Equations in Two Variables

Tables, graphs, and equations are three different ways to represent the relationship between two variables.

Discrete and Continuous Data

Data can be described by the type of coordinates that define them. If the problem context includes all of the values within a range of data, the data are continuous. If the problem context includes values that are distinct or have distinct intervals, the data are discrete.

▶ **Think About It** If the data flow continuously—including all data points in the interval—the data are said to be **continuous**. If the data include a set of points in an interval, but not all points in the interval make sense, the data are called **discrete**.

EXAMPLE 1

Identify the data shown in the table of values as either discrete or continuous.

A

Number of calculators purchased (x)	Total cost (y)
1	$8
2	$16
3	$24
4	$32
5	$40

SOLUTION

The variable x represents the number of calculators purchased. It is not possible to purchase 2.5 calculators. The x-values, in this case, must be limited to whole numbers. Therefore, the data are discrete.

▶ **Remember** The x-values for a relationship representing discrete data are limited.

B

Time in minutes (x)	Number of words typed (y)
1	45
2	90
3	135
4	180
5	225

SOLUTION

The variable x represents the time in minutes. Although the times are shown using only whole numbers, you can also count number of words typed in a partial minute. Therefore, the data are continuous. ▪

Representing Data

Two-variable data also can be represented with graphs and equations. A graph displays the pairs of values visually. An equation shows an algebraic relationship between the variables.

EXAMPLE 2

A Show the data in the table as a graph. Describe the graph of discrete data points.

Number of calculators purchased (x)	Total cost (y)
1	$8
2	$16
3	$24
4	$32
5	$40

▶ **Think About It** Graph the points shown in the table, and then decide if there are other points that also represent the relationship.

SOLUTION

This graph shows five data points. Notice that all values are separate points that cannot be connected because you cannot buy a partial calculator—for instance, 2.25 calculators. So the graph shows discrete data points that are not connected.

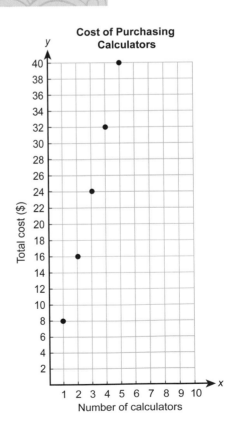

Cost of Purchasing Calculators

B Show the data in the table as a graph. Describe the graph of continuous data points.

Time in minutes (x)	Number of words typed (y)
1	45
2	90
3	135
4	180
5	225

SOLUTION

The graph of typing speed shows the five points from the table, but it also shows that the points can be connected because the data are continuous. For example, approximately 150 words can be typed in 3.5 min. So a graph of continuous data shows data points that are connected.

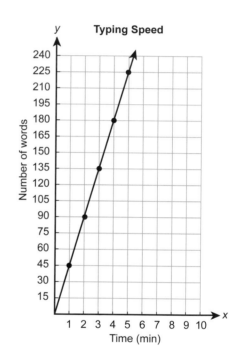

C Write an equation for Examples 2A and 2B.

SOLUTION

> ▶ **Q&A**
>
> **Q** Study each x-y pair in the cost of calculators table. What do all the pairs have in common?
>
> **A** All x-values are multiplied by 8 to get y.

The equation for the calculator data in Example 2A is $y = 8x$, because each x-value is multiplied by 8 to get the corresponding y-value.

The equation for the typing speed data in Example 2B is $y = 45x$, because each x-value is multiplied by 45 to get the corresponding y-value. ■

Independent and Dependent Variables

In two-variable data, the value of one variable often depends on the other.

EXAMPLE 3

Determine which variables are dependent and independent for the tables and graphs shown in Examples 2A and 2B.

A calculator and cost data

> ▶ **Think About It** Does it make more sense that the cost depends on number of calculators, or the number of calculators depends on the cost?

SOLUTION
The value of the dependent variable depends on the value of the independent variable. Because the total cost depends on the number of calculators purchased, the number of calculators is the independent variable, and the total cost is the dependent variable.

SOLUTION

The number of words typed is determined by the amount of time spent typing. So, the number of words typed is the dependent variable, and time is the independent variable. ■

▶ **Think About It** Notice that in both situations, the independent variable is the x-value, and the dependent variable is the y-value. On the graphs, notice that the x-axis represents the independent variables and the y-axis represents the dependent variables.

Ratios, Rates, and Percents

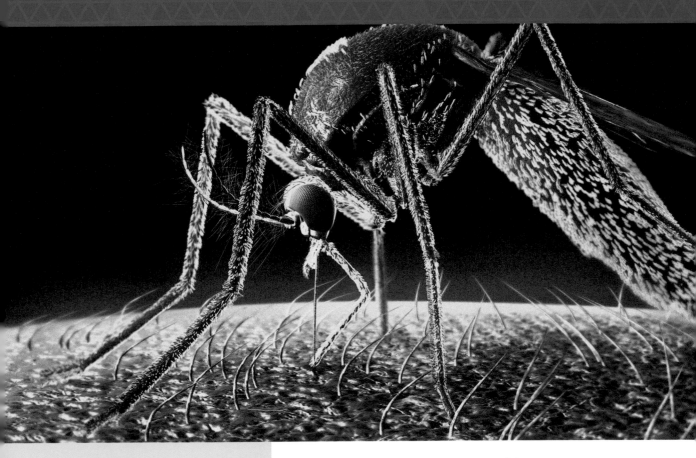

Topic List

In Asia, South America, and Africa, some mosquitoes carry the disease malaria. Scientists and doctors use ratios and rates to compare how efforts to fight malaria are progressing in various countries.

Ratios as Comparisons

You use ratios to compare related quantities, such as the ingredients of a recipe.

Writing Ratios

Definition
A **ratio** is a way of using division to compare two values. The ratio of a to b can be written in three ways. a to b $\quad$ $a : b$ $\quad$ $\dfrac{a}{b}$

You can write a ratio to compare different quantities or different parts of the same whole. When you use a fraction bar, the first value that you are comparing goes on top and the second value goes on the bottom. Simplify the ratio, if possible.

EXAMPLE 1

Write the ratio in three different ways.

A There are 16 fiction books and 13 nonfiction books on the shelf. Write the ratio of nonfiction to fiction books.

SOLUTION

$$\frac{\text{nonfiction}}{\text{fiction}} = \frac{13}{16}$$

also 13 to 16 *or* 13 : 16

The ratio of nonfiction to fiction books can be written as $\dfrac{13}{16}$, 13 to 16, or 13 : 16.

> ▶ **Think About It** The order of the terms is important when you write a ratio. In Example 1A, nonfiction to fiction is 13 to 16, but fiction to nonfiction is 16 to 13.

B An 8-acre park has 6 acres of forest. Write the ratio of the acres of forest to the total acres of the park.

SOLUTION

$$\frac{\text{acres of forest}}{\text{total acres}} = \frac{6}{8} = \frac{6 \div 2}{8 \div 2} = \frac{3}{4}$$

also 3 to 4 *or* 3 : 4

The ratio of acres of forest to total acres can be written as $\frac{3}{4}$, 3 to 4, or 3 : 4. ▪

Writing Ratios for Values with Different Units

It often is a good idea to write both values being compared in a ratio with the same units.

EXAMPLE 2

Write a ratio comparing 50 cm to 2 m.

SOLUTION

Convert meters to centimeters so that the units are the same.

1 m = 100 cm; 2 m = 2 • 100 cm = 200 cm

$$\frac{50 \text{ cm}}{2 \text{ m}} = \frac{50 \text{ cm}}{200 \text{ cm}}$$

$$= \frac{50 \div 50}{200 \div 50} = \frac{1}{4}$$

The ratio of 50 cm to 2 m is $\frac{1}{4}$ or 1 to 4. Because the units for the first and second number are the same, you can drop the units completely. If they were different, you would need to include the units in the answer. ▪

EXAMPLE 3

Write a simplified ratio comparing the two quantities within one system of measurement.

A 6 ft to 10 yd

SOLUTION

Convert yards to feet so that the units are the same.

1 yd = 3 ft; 10 yd = 10 • 3 ft = 30 ft

$$\frac{6 \text{ ft}}{10 \text{ yd}} = \frac{6 \text{ ft}}{30 \text{ ft}}$$

$$= \frac{6 \div 6}{30 \div 6}$$

$$= \frac{1}{5}$$

The ratio of 6 ft to 10 yd is $\frac{1}{5}$ or 1 to 5.

B 30 qt to 5 gal

SOLUTION

Convert gallons to quarts so that the units are the same.

1 gal = 4 qt; 5 gal = 5 • 4 qt = 20 qt

$$\frac{30 \text{ qt}}{5 \text{ gal}} = \frac{30 \text{ qt}}{20 \text{ qt}}$$

$$= \frac{30 \div 10}{20 \div 10}$$

$$= \frac{3}{2}$$

The ratio of 30 qt to 5 gal is $\frac{3}{2}$ or 3 to 2. ■

EXAMPLE 4

Write a simplified ratio comparing the two quantities across two systems of measurement.

A 4 km to 20 mi (Use 1 mi ≈ 1.6 km.)

SOLUTION

Convert miles to kilometers so that the units are the same.

20 mi ≈ 20 • 1.6 km ≈ 32 km

$$\frac{4 \text{ km}}{20 \text{ mi}} \approx \frac{4 \text{ km}}{32 \text{ km}}$$

$$\approx \frac{4 \div 4}{32 \div 4}$$

$$\approx \frac{1}{8}$$

The ratio of 4 km to 20 mi is approximately $\frac{1}{8}$ or 1 to 8.

B 50 in. to 15 cm (Use 1 in. ≈ 2.54 cm.)

SOLUTION

Convert inches to centimeters so that the units are the same.

50 in. ≈ 50 • 2.54 cm ≈ 127 cm

$$\frac{50 \text{ in.}}{15 \text{ cm}} \approx \frac{127 \text{ cm}}{15 \text{ cm}}$$

$$\approx \frac{127}{15}$$

The ratio of 50 in. to 15 cm is approximately $\frac{127}{15}$ or 127 to 15. ■

EXAMPLE 5

Convert each measurement, then write a simplified ratio.

> ▶ **Think About It** Sometimes it helps to convert each measurement before simplifying the ratio.

A 6 km to 9000 mm

SOLUTION

Convert both measurements to meters.

6 km: 1 km = 1000 m

6 km = 6 • 1000 m = 6000 m

9000 mm: 1 mm = $\dfrac{1}{1000}$ m

9000 mm = $\dfrac{9000}{1000}$ m = 9 m

Write and simplify a ratio.

$$\dfrac{6\ km}{9000\ mm} = \dfrac{6000\ m}{9\ m}$$
$$= \dfrac{6000 \div 3}{9 \div 3}$$
$$= \dfrac{2000}{3}$$

The ratio of 6 km to 9000 mm is $\dfrac{2000}{3}$ or 2000 to 3.

B 6 in. to 4 yd

SOLUTION

Convert yards to feet and then to inches.

1 yd = 3 ft; 4 yd = 4 • 3 ft = 12 ft

1 ft = 12 in.; 12 • 12 in. = 144 in.

4 yd = 144 in.

Write and simplify a ratio.

$$\dfrac{6\ in.}{4\ yd} = \dfrac{6\ in.}{144\ in.}$$
$$= \dfrac{6 \div 6}{144 \div 6}$$
$$= \dfrac{1}{24}$$

The ratio of 6 in. to 4 yd is $\dfrac{1}{24}$ or 1 to 24. ■

Solving Problems with Ratios

To find ratios, you need to pay close attention to the parts being compared and the order in which they are compared. Writing a verbal model—the ratio written in words showing what is being compared—is often helpful.

EXAMPLE 6

Look at the figure. Some parts are shaded and some are not.

A Write the ratio of unshaded parts to shaded parts.

SOLUTION

$$\frac{\text{unshaded}}{\text{shaded}} = \frac{4}{3}$$

The ratio of unshaded parts to shaded parts can be written as $\frac{4}{3}$, 4 to 3, or 4 : 3.

B Write the ratio of unshaded parts to total parts.

SOLUTION

$$\frac{\text{unshaded}}{\text{total}} = \frac{4}{7}$$

The ratio of unshaded parts to total parts can be written as $\frac{4}{7}$, 4 to 7, or 4 : 7. ■

EXAMPLE 7

Mark draws 3 yellow circles for every 5 red circles.

A Write the ratio of yellow circles to total circles.

▶ **Think About It** You are not given the total, so you need to add: 3 circles plus 5 circles is 8 circles in all.

SOLUTION

$$\frac{\text{yellow}}{\text{total}} = \frac{3}{8}$$

The ratio of yellow circles to total circles can be written as $\frac{3}{8}$, 3 to 8, or 3 : 8.

B If Mark draws 15 red circles, how many yellow circles would he draw?

▶ **Think About It** Draw groups of 5 red circles until there are 15 of them. For each group of 5 red circles, draw 3 yellow circles.

SOLUTION

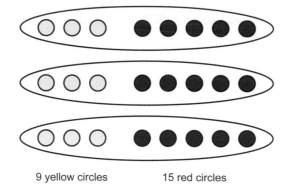

9 yellow circles   15 red circles

There would be 3 groups of 5 red circles and 3 groups of 3 yellow circles. There would be 9 yellow circles. ■

Application: A Recipe

When you increase or decrease one amount in a recipe, the ratios among different ingredients need to stay the same.

EXAMPLE 8

A bread recipe calls for 2 teaspoons of baking soda and 4 cups of flour. How much flour is needed if the recipe is increased to use 6 teaspoons of baking soda?

SOLUTION
Write the ratio of the amount of baking soda used to the amount in the original recipe.

$$\frac{\text{baking soda used}}{\text{baking soda in recipe}} = \frac{6}{2} = \frac{3}{1} = 3$$

Use the ratio to find the amount of flour to be used.

$$3 \cdot 4 \text{ cups} = 12 \text{ cups}$$

With 6 teaspoons of baking soda, the recipe requires 12 cups of flour. ■

Ratio

A ratio is a comparison of two quantities by division. Simplifying ratios can help you compare one ratio to another.

A ratio can be written as a fraction, with a colon, or with the word *to*.

$$\frac{2}{3} \qquad 2:3 \qquad 2 \text{ to } 3$$

▶ **Think About It** All these ratios are read as "2 to 3."

Writing and Simplifying Ratios

To write a ratio in simplest form, write it as a fraction in simplest form.

EXAMPLE 1

Simplify the ratio. Write your answer in all three forms.

 $\frac{8}{10}$

SOLUTION
Simplify the fraction.

$$\frac{8 \div 2}{10 \div 2} = \frac{4}{5} \qquad \text{Divide the numerator and the denominator by the greatest common factor.}$$

$$\frac{4}{5} \text{ or } 4:5 \text{ or } 4 \text{ to } 5$$

B 28 to 4

SOLUTION

Write the ratio as a fraction, and then simplify it.

$$\frac{28}{4} = \frac{28 \div 4}{4 \div 4} = \frac{7}{1}$$

$$\frac{7}{1} \text{ or } 7:1 \text{ or } 7 \text{ to } 1$$

C 63 to 27

SOLUTION

Write the ratio as a fraction, and then simplify it.

$$\frac{63}{27} = \frac{63 \div 9}{27 \div 9} = \frac{7}{3}$$ Don't write a ratio as a mixed number. Write the improper fraction $\frac{7}{3}$.

$$\frac{7}{3} \text{ or } 7:3 \text{ or } 7 \text{ to } 3 \ ▦$$

Equivalent Ratios

Although two ratios may not look the same, they could still be equivalent.

Definition
Equivalent ratios are ratios that describe the same numerical relationship.

How to Check Whether Two Ratios Are Equivalent
To check if two ratios are equivalent, either • Simplify each ratio and compare. If the ratios do not simplify to the same denominator, write each simplified ratio with a common denominator to compare. or • Check to see that the cross products are equal.

EXAMPLE 2

Determine whether the ratios are equivalent.

A $\dfrac{3}{12}, \dfrac{9}{36}$

SOLUTION
Check the values of the cross products.

$$3 \cdot 36 = 12 \cdot 9$$
$$108 = 108$$

Since the cross products are equal, $\dfrac{3}{12}$ is equivalent to $\dfrac{9}{36}$.

B $\dfrac{2}{5}, \dfrac{12}{20}, \dfrac{10}{25}$

> ▶ **Q&A**
>
> **Q** How do you simplify the ratios?
>
> **A** Divide the numerator and denominator by the greatest common factor.

SOLUTION
Simplify two of the ratios and then compare.

$$\dfrac{2}{5} \qquad \dfrac{12 \div 4}{20 \div 4} = \dfrac{3}{5} \qquad \dfrac{10 \div 5}{25 \div 5} = \dfrac{2}{5}$$

The three ratios $\dfrac{2}{5}, \dfrac{12}{20}$, and $\dfrac{10}{25}$ are not equivalent. However, $\dfrac{2}{5}$ and $\dfrac{10}{25}$ are equivalent ratios, because $\dfrac{10}{25}$ simplifies to $\dfrac{2}{5}$. ■

Comparing Ratios

Just as two fractions can be compared, two ratios can also be compared.
Rewrite the ratios with the same denominator and compare the numerators.

EXAMPLE 3

Compare the ratios. Write $<$, $>$, or $=$.

A $\dfrac{5}{14}$ ▪ $\dfrac{1}{4}$

SOLUTION

Rewrite both ratios with a denominator of 28 and then compare.

$$\frac{5 \cdot 2}{14 \cdot 2} = \frac{10}{28} \qquad \frac{1 \cdot 7}{4 \cdot 7} = \frac{7}{28}$$

$$\frac{10}{28} > \frac{7}{28}$$

So $\dfrac{5}{14} > \dfrac{1}{4}$ because 10 is greater than 7.

B $\dfrac{5}{6}$ ▪ $\dfrac{7}{8}$

SOLUTION

Rewrite both ratios with a denominator of 24 and then compare.

$$\frac{5 \cdot 4}{6 \cdot 4} = \frac{20}{24} \qquad \frac{7 \cdot 3}{8 \cdot 3} = \frac{21}{24}$$

$$\frac{20}{24} < \frac{21}{24}$$

So $\dfrac{5}{6} < \dfrac{7}{8}$ because 20 is less than 21. ▪

Tables and Graphs of Equivalent Ratios

You can use a table to show a group of equivalent ratios.

EXAMPLE 4

The table shows equivalent ratios. Each row in the table shows a ratio.

Number of tickets sold	Money collected
1	$4
5	$20
	$28
10	
	$48

A Complete the table.

> **Think About It** To find amount of money collected, multiply number of tickets by 4. To find number of tickets, divide amount of money by 4.

SOLUTION

The number of tickets sold is multiplied by 4 to get the amount of money collected. Use this pattern to complete the table.

Multiply 10 by 4 to get 40.

Divide 28 and 48 by 4 to get 7 and 12.

Number of tickets sold	Money collected
1	$4
5	$20
7	$28
10	**$40**
12	$48

B Graph the ordered pairs from the table.

SOLUTION

Use the table to write the coordinates $(1, 4)$, $(5, 20)$, $(7, 28)$, $(10, 40)$, and $(12, 48)$. Plot the points.

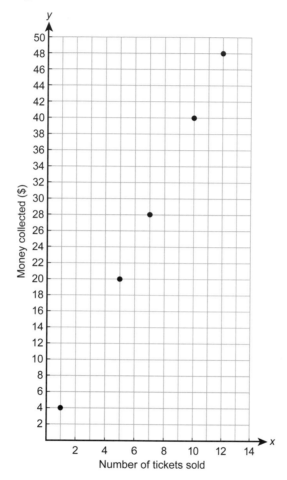

Notice that the points follow the path of a line. ■

> **Think About It** Imagine drawing a line to connect the points. Any point on the line represents one of the ratios in the set. For example, $(1, 4)$ fits in this set and is equivalent to the other ratios represented on the line. But the data are discrete because you cannot buy a partial ticket.

Comparing Parts and Wholes

You can use a ratio to compare a part to a part, a part to a whole, or a whole to a part.

EXAMPLE 5

A jar contains 21 marbles: 8 white, 3 green, and 10 red. Write the described ratio in simplest form.

A number of white marbles to number of green marbles

SOLUTION
There are 8 white marbles and 3 green marbles.

The ratio is $\frac{8}{3}$, or 8 : 3, or 8 to 3.

B number of green marbles to total number of marbles

SOLUTION
There are 3 green marbles and 21 marbles in all.

Since $\frac{3}{21} = \frac{1}{7}$, the ratio is $\frac{1}{7}$, or 1 : 7, or 1 to 7.

C total number of marbles to number of white marbles

SOLUTION
There are 21 marbles in all and 8 white marbles.

The ratio is $\frac{21}{8}$, or 21 : 8, or 21 to 8. ■

▶ **Think About It** Example 5A compares a part to a part. Example 5B compares a part to a whole. Example 5C compares a whole to a part.

Application: Win-Loss Ratio

EXAMPLE 6

A softball team wins 12 of its 22 games, and loses the rest. What is the ratio of wins to losses in simplest form?

> ▶ **Remember** A ratio is not usually written as a mixed number or decimal, but a ratio can contain a mixed number or decimal.

SOLUTION

$22 - 12 = 10$, so the team loses 10 games.

$$\frac{\text{number of wins}}{\text{number of losses}} = \frac{12}{10}$$

$\dfrac{12 \div 2}{10 \div 2} = \dfrac{6}{5}$ Divide by the greatest common factor to simplify the fraction.

The ratio of wins to losses is $\dfrac{6}{5}$, or 6 : 5, or 6 to 5. ■

Ratios as Rates

Ratios can be used to express rates and solve problems involving rates.

Writing Rates to Represent Situations

A **rate** is a ratio of quantities that have different units. For example, 80 mi to 2 h is a rate.

EXAMPLE 1

Write a rate to represent the situation.

A It costs $3 for a 5 min phone call.

SOLUTION

$$\frac{\$3}{5 \text{ min}}$$

B A car travels 85 mi on 4 gal of gasoline.

SOLUTION

$$\frac{85 \text{ mi}}{4 \text{ gal}}$$

▶ **Think About It** It is also correct, in some contexts, to use the reciprocal as the ratio as well, such as the ratio $\frac{4 \text{ gal}}{85 \text{ mi}}$ for Example 1B.

C Three T-shirts cost $17.50.

SOLUTION

$$\frac{\$17.50}{3 \text{ shirts}} \quad \blacksquare$$

Finding Unit Rates

Definition
A **unit rate** is a rate in which the second quantity is 1.

How to Find a Unit Rate
Step 1 Separate the units from the number part of the fraction.
Step 2 Simplify the number part of the fraction.

EXAMPLE 2

Write a unit rate for the situation.

A Mr. Beck drives 120 mi in 3 h.

SOLUTION
Write a ratio. Divide the numerator and denominator by 3.

$$\frac{120}{3} \cdot \frac{\text{miles}}{\text{hours}} = \frac{120 \div 3}{3 \div 3} \cdot \frac{\text{miles}}{\text{hours}} = \frac{40}{1} \cdot \frac{\text{miles}}{\text{hours}}, \text{ or } 40 \text{ mi per } 1 \text{ h}$$

B There are 36 servings in 4 bags.

SOLUTION
Write a ratio. Divide the numerator and denominator by 4.

$$\frac{36}{4} \cdot \frac{\text{servings}}{\text{bags}} = \frac{36 \div 4}{4 \div 4} \cdot \frac{\text{servings}}{\text{bags}} = \frac{9}{1} \cdot \frac{\text{servings}}{\text{bags}}, \text{ or } 9 \text{ servings per bag}$$

C Ella types 474 words in 6 min.

SOLUTION

Write a ratio. Divide the numerator and denominator by 6.

$$\frac{474}{6} \cdot \frac{\text{words}}{\text{minutes}} = \frac{474 \div 6}{6 \div 6} \cdot \frac{\text{words}}{\text{minutes}} = \frac{79}{1} \cdot \frac{\text{words}}{\text{minute}}, \text{ or } 79 \text{ words per min} \blacksquare$$

Describing Unit-Rate Relationships

Translating rates into unit rates is helpful when describing a relationship.

EXAMPLE 3

Ronin is making a granola mix for his camping trip. The recipe calls for 2 cups of mixed nuts and 5 cups of granola. What is the unit rate? What is the meaning of the unit rate?

SOLUTION

The unit rate is $\dfrac{2 \text{ cups of mixed nuts}}{5 \text{ cups of granola}} = \dfrac{\frac{2}{5} \text{ cup of mixed nuts}}{1 \text{ cup of granola}}$.

For every 1 cup of granola, there should be $\frac{2}{5}$ cup of mixed nuts. $\blacksquare$

EXAMPLE 4

The table compares number of miles that a family traveled on a road trip. What is the unit rate? In this context, what is the meaning of the unit rate?

Number of hours driving	Number of miles traveled
2	120
3	180
4	240
5	300

SOLUTION

Use one of the rates from the table to find the unit rate.

$$\frac{120 \text{ mi} \div 2}{2 \text{ h} \div 2} = \frac{60 \text{ mi}}{1 \text{ h}}$$

The family traveled at a rate of 60 mi per 1 h. ■

Application: Fuel Economy

EXAMPLE 5

A car travels 255 mi and uses 8.5 gal of gasoline. Write the unit rate that describes the car's fuel economy.

SOLUTION

Write a rate, and then convert it to a unit rate.

$$\frac{255}{8.5} \cdot \frac{\text{miles}}{\text{gallons}} = \frac{255 \div 8.5}{8.5 \div 8.5} \cdot \frac{\text{miles}}{\text{gallons}} = \frac{30}{1} \cdot \frac{\text{miles}}{\text{gallon}}$$

The car's fuel economy is described by the unit rate 30 mi per 1 gal. ■

Unit Rates

Unit rates help you solve problems involving distance, work, and price.

Finding the Unit Rate

To find a unit rate, divide the first term of the rate by the second term of the rate.

EXAMPLE 1

Find the unit rate.

A 12 servings for 6 people

SOLUTION

Write the rate. Divide the first term by the second term.

$$\frac{12 \text{ servings}}{6 \text{ people}} = \frac{12}{6} \text{ servings/person} = \frac{2}{1} \text{ servings/person}$$
$$= 2 \text{ servings/person}$$

The unit rate is $\dfrac{2 \text{ servings}}{1 \text{ person}}$ or 2 servings per 1 person.

B 10 km in 4 h

SOLUTION

Write the rate. Divide the first term by the second term.

$$\frac{10 \text{ km}}{4 \text{ h}} = \frac{10}{4} \text{ km/h} = 2\frac{1}{2} \text{ km/h} = 2.5 \text{ km/h}$$

The unit rate is $\dfrac{2.5 \text{ km}}{1 \text{ h}}$, or 2.5 km/h, or $2\frac{1}{2}$ km per 1 h. ■

Using Unit Rates to Solve Problems

Many times, it is easier to use the unit rate rather than the given rate to solve a problem.

EXAMPLE 2

A Miguel can ride his bike 3 mi in 15 min. If he rides at the same speed, how long will it take him to ride 12 mi?

SOLUTION
Find the unit rate. Use it to help find the answer.

$$\frac{15 \text{ min}}{3 \text{ mi}} = \frac{15}{3} \text{ min/mi} = 5 \text{ min/mi} \qquad \text{It takes Miguel 5 min to ride 1 mi.}$$

Use the unit rate to find the total time.

$$\text{minutes} = \frac{\text{minutes}}{\text{mile}} \cdot \text{miles}$$

$$= (5 \text{ min/mi}) \cdot (12 \text{ mi}) \qquad \text{Multiply the unit rate by 12 mi.}$$

$$= 60 \text{ min}$$

It will take Miguel 60 min to ride 12 mi.

B Denzel makes crafts to sell at art shows. He times himself and finds he can make 12 crafts in 4 h. How long will it take Denzel to make 48 crafts?

SOLUTION
Find the unit rate. Use it to help find the answer.

$$\frac{12 \text{ crafts}}{4 \text{ h}} = \frac{12}{4} \text{ crafts/h} = 3 \text{ crafts/h} \qquad \text{He can make 3 crafts in 1 h.}$$

Use the unit rate to find the total time. The simple rate equation is total crafts = rate • time.

You want to know the time, so write an equivalent equation with time alone on one side.

$$\text{time} = \text{total crafts} \div \text{rate}$$

Substitute and simplify.

$\text{hours} = 48 \text{ crafts} \div \dfrac{3 \text{ crafts}}{1 \text{ h}}$ Divide 48 by the unit rate.

$\text{hours} = 48 \text{ crafts} \cdot \dfrac{1 \text{ h}}{3 \text{ crafts}} = 16 \text{ hours}$ Multiply by the reciprocal of the unit rate.

It will take Denzel 16 h to make 48 crafts. ■

Solving Unit-Rate Problems

Although some unit rates involve only whole numbers, unit rates can also include decimals.

Finding Both Unit Rates

You can find two different unit rates for any given pair of measures. Divide the first measure by the second to find one unit rate. Then divide the second measure by the first to find the other unit rate.

EXAMPLE 1

Find both unit rates for the pair of measures.

A $11.16 for 4 gal of gas

SOLUTION
Divide dollars by gallons.

$$\frac{\$11.16}{4 \text{ gal}} = \frac{11.16}{4} \text{ dollars/gal} = 2.79 \text{ dollars/gal}$$

Divide gal by dollars.

$$\frac{4 \text{ gal}}{\$11.16} = \frac{4}{11.16} \text{ gal/dollars} \approx 0.358 \text{ gal/dollar}$$

The unit rates are $2.79/gal and 0.358 gal per 1 dollar.

▶ **Think About It** The two unit rates will be reciprocals.

B 499.2 mi in 8 h

SOLUTION

Divide miles by hours.

$$\frac{499.2 \text{ mi}}{8 \text{ h}} = \frac{499.2}{8} \text{ mi/h} = 62.4 \text{ mi/h}$$

Divide hours by miles.

$$\frac{8 \text{ h}}{499.2 \text{ mi}} = \frac{8}{499.2} \text{ h/mi} \approx 0.016 \text{ h/mi}$$

The unit rates are 62.4 mi/h and 0.016 h per 1 mi. ▪

Using Unit Rates to Solve Problems

Unit rates can help you find the best price when items are packaged differently.

EXAMPLE 2

Marco can buy 3 bottles of olive oil for a total of $36.30 or a case of 12 bottles for $118.80. Which is the better deal?

SOLUTION

Find and compare the unit prices.

unit price for 3 bottles:

$$\frac{\$36.30}{3 \text{ bottles}} = \frac{36.30}{3} \text{ dollars/bottles} = 12.10 \text{ dollars/bottle}$$

unit price for case of 12 bottles:

$$\frac{\$118.80}{12 \text{ bottles}} = \frac{118.80}{12} \text{ dollars/bottles} = 9.90 \text{ dollars/bottle}$$

Since $9.90/bottle is less than $12.10/bottle, the better deal is the case with 12 bottles for $118.80. ▪

You can select whichever of the two rates will make it easier to solve the problem.

EXAMPLE 3

Paul drove his car 268.2 mi in 6 h. Which unit rate is better to use to find how far Paul could drive in 11 h?

SOLUTION

Decide whether you will need to multiply or divide with each unit rate.

If the rate is in mi/h, multiply to find the distance.

$$\text{miles} = \text{hours} \cdot \frac{\text{miles}}{\text{hour}}$$

If the rate is in h/mi, divide to find the distance.

$$\text{miles} = \text{hours} \div \frac{\text{hours}}{\text{mile}}$$

Multiplication is easier than division, so choose the unit rate that allows you to do that.

Use the unit rate for mi/h to solve the problem. ▪

Average-Speed Problems

Unit rates can help you solve problems about distance, time, and speed.

Using Rate Tables to Show Speed

One special type of unit rate is speed. The first quantity in the rate is a distance. The second quantity is a time. For example, a speed of 50 miles per hour can be written as the unit rate 50 mi/1 h, or 50 mi/h, or 50 mph.

Definition
Speed is the ratio of distance traveled to time.

▶ **Think About It** The word *per* is often used to describe speed.

EXAMPLE 1

This rate table shows Akira's hiking at 4 mph. Complete the table to show equivalent speeds. Then use it to find the distance covered in 10 h.

Distance (mi)	4				
Time (h)	1	2	3	6	10

SOLUTION

The rate for the speed is **4 : 1**. Multiply both terms of the rate by 2, then by 3, and so on.

		4 • 2 ↓	**4 • 3** ↓	**4 • 6** ↓	**4 • 10** ↓
Distance (mi)	4				
Time (h)	1	2	3	6	10

Akira will hike 40 mi in 10 h. ▪

Using the Distance Formula

The formula $r = \dfrac{d}{t}$ shows that speed is the ratio of distance to time.

Distance Formula

For a moving object traveling a distance d at speed r for time t:

$$d = rt \qquad r = \frac{d}{t} \qquad t = \frac{d}{r}$$

▶ **Think About It** The variable r can be used for speed. The r reminds you that speed is a rate.

EXAMPLE 2

Write and evaluate an expression to find the time or the speed.

A $r = 35$ mi/h, $d = 175$ mi

SOLUTION

You are given the speed and the distance. Use $t = \dfrac{d}{r}$ to find the time.

$t = \dfrac{d}{r}$ Write the formula.

$\quad = 175$ mi $\div$ 35 mi/h   Substitute.

$\quad = 5$ h   Divide.

> ▶ **Think About It** Instead of memorizing three formulas, you can always use $d = rt$ and solve for the distance, rate, or time.

B $t = 10$ min, $d = 3.2$ m

SOLUTION

You are given the time and the distance. Use $r = \dfrac{d}{t}$ to find the speed.

$r = \dfrac{d}{t}$ Write the formula.

$\quad = \dfrac{3.2 \text{ m}}{10 \text{ min}}$ Substitute.

$\quad = 0.32$ m/min   Divide. ▪

Application: Average Speed

To find average speed, divide the total distance by the total time.

EXAMPLE 3

The Changs sailed 30 km in 6 h, stopped for lunch, and then sailed 15 km in 5 h. Find their average sailing speed.

SOLUTION

Find the total distance.

$$30 + 15 = 45$$

Find the total time.

$$6 + 5 = 11$$

Use $r = \dfrac{d}{t}$ to find the speed.

$r = \dfrac{45 \text{ km}}{11 \text{ h}}$ Substitute.

$r \approx 4.1 \text{ km/h}$ Divide.

The average speed was about 4.1 km/h. ■

Constant-Rate Problems

Problems about constant rates can be solved with tables or equations.

Using Rate Tables

A speed such as miles/hour is one kind of rate. Many other types of rates exist. Rates that don't change over time are called constant.

Definition
A rate is a **constant rate** if it does not change over time.

▶ **Think About It** To use a rate table for problems with constant rates, multiply both terms of the rate by the same number.

EXAMPLE 1

This table shows data that increase at a constant rate. Find the values of y when x = 10, 11, and 32.

y	24	48	72			
x	2	4	6	10	11	32

SOLUTION

Find the constant rate. Then multiply the x-values by the constant rate to find the corresponding y-values.

Divide to find the constant rate.

$$24 \div 2 = 12$$
$$48 \div 4 = 12$$
$$72 \div 6 = 12$$

The constant rate is 12.

▶ **Q&A**

Q Each y-value is divided by what number to get the x-value?

A 12, which is the constant rate

Multiply the constant rate by the x-value to find the missing y-values.

$$12 \cdot 10 = 120$$
$$12 \cdot 11 = 132$$
$$12 \cdot 32 = 384$$

Complete the table.

y	24	48	72	**120**	**132**	**384**
x	2	4	6	10	11	32

EXAMPLE 2

This tape diagram shows a constant rate when $x = 3$ and the related values of y. Find the values of y when $x = 5, 9,$ and 48.

x	3	6	9	12	15	18	21	24	27
y		9			18			27	

SOLUTION

Find the constant rate. Then use the rate to find the y-values.

The diagram shows 3 x's for every y. The constant rate is 3, so multiply each x-value by 3.

Multiply.

$$3 \cdot 5 = 15$$
$$3 \cdot 9 = 27$$
$$3 \cdot 48 = 144$$

When $x = 5$, $y = 15$.

When $x = 9$, $y = 27$.

When $x = 48$, $y = 144$. ■

EXAMPLE 3

When $x = 6$, $y = 30$. When $x = 12$, $y = 60$. The rate is always constant. Use a double number line to answer the questions.

A What is y when $x = 24$?

SOLUTION

Make a double number line (one line for x, one line for y). Line up 6 on the line for x with 30 on the line for y. Line up 12 on the line for x with 60 on the line for y.

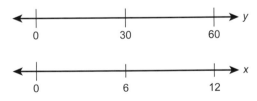

Notice the line for y counts by 30, and the line for x counts by 6. Extend the lines and follow the pattern.

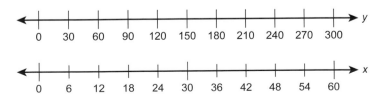

Find 24 on the number line for x. It matches up with 120 on the line for y. When $x = 24$, $y = 120$.

B What is x when $y = 210$?

SOLUTION

Find 210 on the number line for y. It matches up with 42 on the line for x. When $y = 210$, $x = 42$. ■

EXAMPLE 4

A This rate table shows a factory machine that fills bottles at a constant rate. Find the number of bottles filled in 60 min.

Number of bottles	40				
Time (min)	1	5	10	20	60

SOLUTION

The production rate for the machine is 40 bottles per minute. Multiply each time by 40 to complete the top row of the table.

Number of bottles	40	200	400	800	2400
Time (min)	1	5	10	20	60

The machine will fill 2400 bottles in 60 min.

B Another machine at the bottle factory fills 300 bottles in 5 min. How many bottles does it fill in 8 min?

> **Think About It** The machine in Example 4B is faster because it has a greater unit rate.

SOLUTION

Find the unit rate, and then multiply by 8 min.

Divide to find the unit rate.

$$(300 \text{ bottles}) \div (5 \text{ min}) = 60 \text{ bottles/min}$$

Multiply the rate by time.

$$(60 \text{ bottles/min}) \cdot (8 \text{ min}) = 480 \text{ bottles}$$

This machine fills 480 bottles in 8 min. ■

Using the Work Formula

Many problems involve finding how long it takes to do a task at a constant rate of work. To solve these problems, use the work formula.

Work Formula
If w is the amount of work done, r is the constant rate, and t is the time worked, then $$w = rt.$$

To solve work problems, translate to an equation. Look at the units to make sure you are using the correct form of the equation. Then solve.

EXAMPLE 5

Use the work formula to find the work done, the rate of work, or the time worked.

A rate = 6 mi of road paved per day, time = 5 days

SOLUTION

You are given the rate and the time. Find the work.

$$\text{miles paved of road} = \frac{\text{miles of road}}{\text{day}} \cdot \text{days}$$

$w = rt$ Write the formula.

$= \dfrac{6 \text{ mi}}{\text{day}} \cdot 5 \text{ days}$ Substitute.

$= 30 \text{ mi}$ Multiply.

The work was the paving of 30 mi of road.

B A pipe can fill a 3000 gal tank in 12 h.

SOLUTION

You are given the time and the work. Find the rate.

$$\text{gallons filled} = \frac{\text{gallons}}{\text{hour}} \cdot \text{hours}$$

$w = rt$ Write the formula.

$3000 \text{ gal} = r \cdot 12 \text{ h}$ Substitute.

$\dfrac{3000 \text{ gal}}{12 \text{ h}} = \dfrac{r \cdot 12 \text{ h}}{12 \text{ h}}$ Divide both sides of the equation by 12 h.

$\dfrac{250 \text{ gal}}{1 \text{ h}} = r$ Simplify.

The rate for the pipe filling the tank is 250 gal/h. ▪

Finding Percents of Numbers

You can use percent to find a part if you know the whole. You can also use percent to find a whole if you know the part.

Finding the Percent of a Number

You can find a given percent of a whole number by first converting the percent to a decimal or a fraction. Then multiply the decimal or the fraction by the whole number.

You can use a model to help you find the percent of a number.

EXAMPLE 1

What is 25% of 80?

SOLUTION
You can use a double number line to find 25% of 80.

Both number lines will start at 0. The top number line should end at 80 and the percent number line should end at 100%.

Plot 25% on the percent number line. Since $100 \div 25 = 4$, divide both number lines into 4 equal parts.

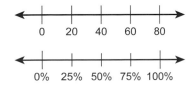

Since $80 \div 4 = 20$, each part in the top number line should represent 20.

To find 25% of 80, locate 25% on the percent number line. Find the corresponding number on the top number line.

So 25% of 80 is 20. ■

EXAMPLE 2

Find the percent of the number.

> ▶ **Remember** Convert a percent to a decimal by moving the decimal point 2 places to the left.
>
> Convert a percent to a fraction by writing a fraction with a denominator of 100. Then simplify if possible.

A 18% of 70

SOLUTION
It probably is easier to use the decimal than the fraction form.

$18\% = 0.18$ Convert the percent to a decimal.

$0.18 \cdot 70 = 12.6$ Multiply.

18% of 70 is 12.6.

CHECK
Use mental math and benchmarks, such as 10% and 20%. When you figure that 10% of 70 is 7, and 20% of 70 is 14, you know that the answer of 12.6 is reasonable.

B 25% of 440

SOLUTION
The percent equals the fraction $\frac{1}{4}$, and multiplying by $\frac{1}{4}$ is probably easier than multiplying by 0.25.

$$25\% = \frac{1}{4}$$ Convert the percent to a fraction.

$$\frac{1}{4} \cdot 440 = 440 \div 4$$ Write an equivalent division problem.

$$= 110$$ Divide.

So 25% of 440 is 110. ▪

Finding the Whole from a Percent

Percent problems often describe a part of a whole. If you are given a percent and a part, you can find the whole by writing a multiplication equation that uses a decimal or a fraction.

EXAMPLE 3

10% of what number is 81?

SOLUTION

You can use a ratio table to find the whole when given a percent and a part.

Set up the table to show equivalent ratios where the part is in one column and the whole is in the other column.

Part	Whole
81	?
10	100

▶ **Q&A**

Q 10 times what equals 100?

A 10; Multiply 81 by 10.

Multiply 10 by 10 to get 100.

Multiply 81 by 10 to get 810.

So 81 is 10% of 810. ▪

EXAMPLE 4

20% of what number is 45?

SOLUTION

Translate the problem into an equation.

20%	of	what number	is	45?
20%	•	n	=	45

$0.2 \cdot n = 45$ Convert the percent to a decimal.

$(0.2 \cdot n) \div 0.2 = 45 \div 0.2$ Divide both sides by 0.2.

$n = 225$ Simplify.

So 20% of 225 is 45. ◾

> ▶ **Think About It** You also could have converted 20% to the fraction $\frac{1}{5}$.
>
> Look at all the numbers in the problem to see whether working with a fraction or a decimal would be easier.

Finding the Percent from the Whole and Part

You can find the percent if you know the part and the whole.

EXAMPLE 5

What percent is 15 out of 25?

> ▶ **Think About It** The percent is unknown. Look for *is* and *of* to find the part and whole. The "*is*" number is usually the part, and the "*of*" number is usually the whole.

SOLUTION

Make a diagram.

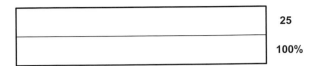

The top bar represents the number, and the bottom bar represents the percent. The whole top represents 25, and the whole bottom represents 100%.

Since you know the part and whole, write $\frac{15}{25}$, and simplify to $\frac{3}{5}$. Divide each bar of the diagram into 5 parts. Five groups of 5 equal 25, and 5 groups of 20% equal 100%.

5	5	5	5	5	25
20%	20%	20%	20%	20%	100%

Shade 3 boxes on the top to show 15. Shade the same number of boxes on the bottom. Note that 60% is shaded.

So 15 is 60% of 25. ◼

You can also write the relationship between a part and a whole as a fraction.

$$\frac{\text{part}}{\text{whole}} = \text{part} \div \text{whole}$$

You can also think of this relationship as an equation.

$$\text{percent} \times \text{whole} = \text{part}$$

EXAMPLE 6

What percent of 125 is 95?

SOLUTION

Translate the problem into an equation.

What percent	of	125	is	95?
P	$\times$	125	$=$	95

$P \times 125 = 95$

$P \times 125 \div \mathbf{125} = 95 \div \mathbf{125}$ Divide both sides by 125.

$P = 0.76$ Divide.

$P = 0.76 \cdot 100$ Convert to percent.

$P = 76\%$ Multiply.

So 95 is 76% of 125. ■

▶ **Think About It** *Percent* means "hundredths" or "per hundred." After dividing a part by a whole, multiply by 100 to find the percent. Move the decimal point 2 places to the right and write the percent symbol.

EXAMPLE 7

36 is what percent of 75?

▶ **Think About It** "Of 75" means to multiply.

SOLUTION

Translate the problem into an equation.

36	is	what percent	of	75?
36	$=$	?	$\cdot$	75

$36 = ? \cdot 75$

$0.48 = ?$ Divide by 75.

$0.48 \cdot 100 = ?$ Convert to percent.

$48\% = ?$ Multiply.

So 36 is 48% of 75. ■

Solving Problems with Percents

Percents are used widely in everyday settings. An understanding of percents helps in analyzing data, manufacturing goods, shopping, and many other areas.

Application: A Survey

EXAMPLE 1

Twenty people in a survey said the library needs more bike racks. That number was 5% of the total number of people in the survey. How many people were in the survey?

SOLUTION
Translate the situation into a percent problem, and then into an equation. Let $p =$ the total number of people in the survey.

20	is	5%	of	what number?
20	=	5%	•	P

$$20 = 0.05 \cdot p \qquad \text{Convert the percent to a decimal.}$$

$$20 \div \mathbf{0.05} = (0.05 \cdot p) \div \mathbf{0.05} \qquad \text{Divide both sides by 0.05.}$$

$$400 = p \qquad \text{Simplify.}$$

There were 400 people in the survey. ■

Application: Manufacturing

EXAMPLE 2

A company that manufactures bicycles reports 2 out of 50 bicycles are defective. What percent of the bicycles are defective?

SOLUTION

You can use a ratio table to find the whole when given a part and a whole.

Part	Whole
2	50
?	100

Set up the table to show equivalent ratios, where the part is in one column and the whole is in the other column.

Divide 50 by 2 to get 25. Divide 100 by 25 to get 4.

So 4% of the bicycles are defective. ▪

Percents in Circle Graphs

A circle graph shows parts of a whole.

EXAMPLE 3

The members of a club voted for their favorite pet. The circle graph shows the data.

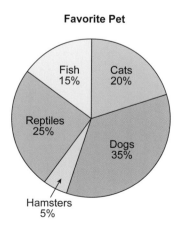

Favorite Pet

Fish 15%
Cats 20%
Reptiles 25%
Dogs 35%
Hamsters 5%

Think About It Notice that the sum of the percent values in the circle graph is 100%.

$$25\% + 15\% + 20\% + 35\% + 5\% = 100\%$$

A What percent of the club chose reptiles as their favorite pet?

SOLUTION
According to the circle graph, 25% of the members chose reptiles as their favorite pet.

B What percent of the club did **not** choose dogs as their favorite pet?

SOLUTION
Since the whole graph represents 100%, and 35% of the club did choose dogs, find 100% − 35%.

So 65% of the members did not choose dogs as their favorite pet. ▪

EXAMPLE 4

The circle graph shows how a group of 500 people who live downtown prefer to get to work.

How many people prefer to walk or ride a bike to work?

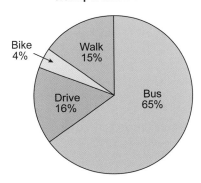

Transportation to Work

Bike 4%
Walk 15%
Drive 16%
Bus 65%

SOLUTION

Add the bikers and walkers to find the percent.

$$4\% + 15\% = 19\%$$

You know the percent (19%) and whole (500 people). Use an equation to find the part—the number of people who prefer to ride a bike or walk to work.

So 19% of 500 represents the number of people who prefer to ride a bike or walk to work.

$$19\% \text{ of } 500 = 19\% \times 500 = 0.19 \times 500 = 95$$

Since 95 is 19% of 500, 95 people prefer to ride a bike or walk to work. ▪

EXAMPLE 5

The circle graph shows what different employees at a certain company did for lunch on Monday, when 3 employees ate the salad bar. How many employees are represented in the entire circle graph?

Lunch on Monday

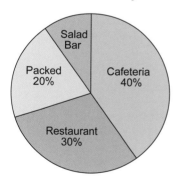

SOLUTION

Find the percent of employees who ate from the salad bar, and use an equation to find the total number of employees represented in the circle graph.

Add the percents of the other three categories.

$$40\% + 30\% + 20\% = 90\%$$
$$100\% - 90\% = 10\%$$

So 10% of the employees ate from the salad bar. There were 3 employees who ate from the salad bar.

10% of how many is 3?

Let T represent the total.

10% of $T = 3$

$\quad 0.1 \cdot T = 3$ Change percent to a decimal.

$\quad \dfrac{0.1 \cdot T}{0.1} = \dfrac{3}{0.1}$ Divide both sides by 0.1.

$\quad\quad\quad T = 30$ Simplify.

There are 30 employees represented in the circle graph. ■

EXAMPLE 6

The circle graph shows the number of students who are beginners, intermediate, or advanced in computer programming. Notice that this graph shows number of students instead of percent of students.

What percent of the students are beginners?

Experience in Programming

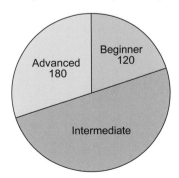

SOLUTION

Notice that half the circle represents intermediate programmers, so the other half represents advanced or beginners. The number of intermediate programmers equals the number of advanced plus beginner programmers.

There are $180 + 120 = 300$ intermediate coders, which is the part.

There are $300 \cdot 2 = 600$ students total.

Find the percent of students who are beginners.

What % of $600 = 120$?

$$P \cdot 600 = 120 \qquad \text{Write the equation.}$$

$$\frac{P \cdot 600}{600} = \frac{120}{600} \qquad \text{Divide both sides by 600.}$$

$$P = 0.2 \qquad \text{Simplify.}$$

$$P = 20\% \qquad \text{Change the decimal to percent.}$$

So 20% of the students are beginners. ∎

Area, Surface Area, and Volume

Topic List

Whether designing a building, assembling a bench, or installing hardwood floors, it's important to be able to compute the area of a surface and the volume of a solid.

Area of Rectangles

You've used the formula $A = s^2$ to find the area of a square with side length s. You can use a similar formula to find the area of any rectangle.

Finding the Area of a Rectangle

Definition

A **rectangle** is a plane figure with four sides and four square corners.

Area of a Rectangle

The area of a rectangle with length l and width w is

$$A = lw.$$

▶ **Think About It** In a rectangle, opposite sides have equal length. A square is a rectangle with $l = w$. So the formula $A = s^2$ is a special case of $A = lw$.

When finding the area of a rectangle, express your answer in square units.

EXAMPLE 1

Find the area of the rectangle.

12 in.

24 in.

▶ **Think About It** The commutative property of multiplication states that the order of the factors does not affect the product.

SOLUTION

$A = lw$

$\quad = 24 \cdot 12$ Substitute 24 for l and 12 for w.

$\quad = 288$ Multiply.

The area is 288 in^2. ■

Choosing Length and Width

The area of a rectangle is the same whether you multiply $l \cdot w$ or $w \cdot l$. So you can use either dimension as the length.

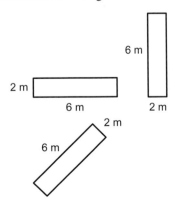

6 m

2 m

6 m

2 m

2 m

6 m

The way the rectangle is turned doesn't matter either. All three of the rectangles shown have the same area. You could use length 6 m and width 2 m or use length 2 m and width 6 m for any of the three.

EXAMPLE 2

Write two equations that you could use to find the area of the rectangle.
Then find the the area both ways.

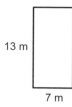

13 m

7 m

SOLUTION

Use the area formula, $A = lw$. Substitute values for l and w.

For $l = 13$ and $w = 7$:

$A = lw$

$= 13 \cdot 7$

$= 91$

For $l = 7$ and $w = 13$:

$A = lw$

$= 7 \cdot 13$

$= 91$

The area of the rectangle can be found using the equation $A = 13 \cdot 7$ or
$A = 7 \cdot 13$. Either way, the area is 91 m^2. ■

Application: Painting Walls

EXAMPLE 3

A painter uses a table to record the dimensions of some walls he will paint.
How many square feet of wall will he paint in all?

Wall Measurements

	Length	Height	Area
Wall 1	22 ft	8 ft	
Wall 2	14 ft	8 ft	
Wall 3	16 ft	10 ft	
Wall 4	9 ft	10 ft	

SOLUTION

Find the area of each wall. Then add to find the total area.

$A_1 = l_1 w_1$

$\quad = 22 \cdot 8$

$\quad = 176$

$A_2 = l_2 w_2$

$\quad = 14 \cdot 8$

$\quad = 112$

$A_3 = l_3 w_3$

$\quad = 16 \cdot 10$

$\quad = 160$

$A_4 = l_4 w_4$

$\quad = 9 \cdot 10$

$\quad = 90$

$A = A_1 + A_2 + A_3 + A_4$

$\quad = 176 + 112 + 160 + 90$

$\quad = 538$

The painter will paint 538 ft^2 of wall. ◾

Areas of Rectangles and Triangles

Every closed figure has an interior.

The interior of the rectangle is the space enclosed by the sides of the rectangle. The interior of this rectangle is shaded.

▶ **Think About It** The *interior* is the *inside* of the figure.

Definition

The **area** of a figure is the number of square units in the interior of the figure.

This rectangle has an area of 32 square units. Notice that 32 is the product of the number of rows, 4, and number of columns, 8.

▶ **Think About It** Area is expressed using square units, such as ft^2 (square feet). When no units are provided, use "square units" or "units^2."

Finding the Area of a Rectangle

EXAMPLE 1

Find the area of the rectangle.

A

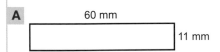

60 mm

11 mm

SOLUTION

Use the formula. The calculation may be performed with or without the units.

Method 1

$A = lw$

$= 60 \cdot 11$ Substitute 60 for l and 11 for w.

$= 660$ Multiply.

The area is 660 mm^2.

Method 2

$A = lw$

$= (60 \text{ mm}) \cdot (11 \text{ mm})$

$= 60 \cdot 11 \cdot \text{mm} \cdot \text{mm}$

$= 660 \text{ mm}^2$

B

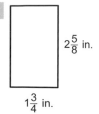

$2\frac{5}{8}$ in.

$1\frac{3}{4}$ in.

SOLUTION
Use the formula.

$A = lw$

$A = 1\frac{3}{4} \cdot 2\frac{5}{8}$ Substitute $1\frac{3}{4}$ for l and $2\frac{5}{8}$ for w.

$A = \frac{7}{4} \cdot \frac{21}{8}$ Rewrite the mixed numbers as improper fractions.

$A = \frac{147}{32}$ Multiply.

$A = 4\frac{19}{32}$ Simplify.

The area of the rectangle is $4\frac{19}{32}$ in^2.

C

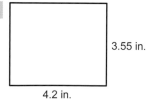

3.55 in.

4.2 in.

SOLUTION
Use the formula.

$A = lw$

$A = \textbf{4.2} \cdot \textbf{3.55}$ Substitute.

$$
\begin{array}{r}
3.55 \\
\times\ 4.2 \\
\hline
710 \\
+14200 \\
\hline
14.910
\end{array}
$$
     Multiply.

$A = 14.91 \text{ in}^2$ Place the decimal point.

> ▶ **Think About It**
> **NOTATION** You can rewrite 14.910 as 14.91.

The area of the rectangle is 14.91 in^2. ◾

EXAMPLE 2

Sarah is planting a garden that measures $6\frac{1}{2}$ ft long by $3\frac{3}{4}$ ft wide.

How many square feet of her yard will the garden cover?

SOLUTION
Use the formula.

$A = lw$

$A = 6\frac{1}{2} \cdot 3\frac{3}{4}$ Substitute.

$A = \dfrac{13}{2} \cdot \dfrac{15}{4}$ Rewrite the mixed numbers as improper fractions.

$A = \dfrac{195}{8}$ Multiply.

$A = 24\frac{3}{8}$ Simplify.

The garden will cover $24\frac{3}{8} \text{ ft}^2$ of Sarah's yard. ◾

EXAMPLE 3

James wants to order new carpet for his living room. The room measures 15.5 ft by 20.25 ft. How many square feet of carpet should he order to cover the entire floor?

SOLUTION

Use the formula for the area of a rectangle to find the square footage of the room. Multiply the decimals using the standard method.

$A = lw$

$A = \mathbf{15.5} \cdot \mathbf{20.25}$ Substitute.

$$
\begin{array}{r}
20.25 \\
\times\ \ 15.5 \\
\hline
10125 \\
101250 \\
+\ 202500 \\
\hline
313.875
\end{array}
$$
     Multiply.

$A = 313.875 \text{ ft}^2$ Place the decimal point.

> ▶ **Think About It**
> **NOTATION** There are 3 decimal places in the factors, so there should be 3 decimal places in the product.

The area of the floor is 313.875 ft^2.

He should order at least 314 ft^2 of carpet. ■

Finding a Missing Dimension

You can use the formula for the area of a rectangle to find a missing dimension. If you know the area and one side length of the figure, you can use the area formula to solve for the missing side length.

EXAMPLE 4

The length of a rectangle is 2.8 m. The area of the rectangle is 29.68 m^2.
What is the width?

SOLUTION
Use the formula for the area of the rectangle. Fill in the given values. Solve
for width.

$A = lw$

$29.68 = 2.8 \cdot w$ Substitute.

$\dfrac{29.68}{2.8} = w$ Divide both sides by 2.8.

$2.8\overline{)29.68} = 28\overline{)296.8}$ Before dividing, multiply the dividend and divisor by 10, so that you can divide by a whole number.

$$
\begin{array}{r}
10.6 \\
28\overline{)296.8} \\
-280.0 \\
\hline
16.0 \\
-0.0 \\
\hline
16.8 \\
-16.8 \\
\hline
0
\end{array}
$$
         Divide.

The width is 10.6 m. ■

> ▶ **Think About It**
> **NOTATION** Label the width as meters. Area is measured in square units, but length and width are measured in units.

EXAMPLE 5

The area of a rectangle is $20\frac{3}{4}$ cm^2. The width of the rectangle is $4\frac{3}{20}$ cm. What is the length?

SOLUTION

Use the formula for the area of the rectangle. Fill in the given values. Solve for length.

$A = lw$	Use the area formula.
$20\frac{3}{4} = l \cdot 4\frac{3}{20}$	Substitute.
$\frac{83}{4} = l \cdot \frac{83}{20}$	Rewrite mixed numbers as improper fractions.
$\frac{83}{4} \div \frac{83}{20} = l \cdot \frac{83}{20} \div \frac{83}{20}$	Divide both sides by $\frac{83}{20}$.
$\frac{83}{4} \cdot \frac{20}{83} = l \cdot \frac{83}{20} \cdot \frac{20}{83}$	Multiply by the reciprocal.
$\frac{\overset{1}{\cancel{83}}}{\underset{1}{\cancel{4}}} \cdot \frac{\overset{5}{\cancel{20}}}{\underset{1}{\cancel{83}}} = l$	Divide out common factors and then multiply.
$5 = l$	Simplify.

The length of the rectangle is 5 cm. ▪

Finding the Area of a Triangle

A triangle is half a rectangle, so the formula for the area of a triangle is half the formula for the rectangle.

Area of a Triangle

The area of a triangle with base b and height h is

$$A = \frac{1}{2}bh$$

or

$$A = \frac{bh}{2}.$$

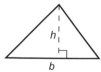

The base of a triangle always forms a right angle with the height of the triangle.

For acute triangles, the height is always shown inside the triangle. For obtuse triangles, it can be located in the exterior of the triangle. In a right triangle, the height can be one of the sides of the triangle.

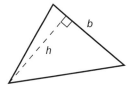 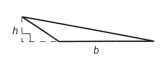 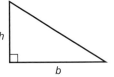

▶ **Think About It** Any side can be used as the base. The height will change accordingly.

EXAMPLE 6

Find the area of the triangle.

25 km

22 km

SOLUTION
Use the formula.

$A = \frac{1}{2}bh$

$= \frac{1}{2} \cdot 22 \cdot 25$ Substitute 22 for b and 25 for h.

$= 11 \cdot 25$ Multiply.

$= 275$ Multiply.

The area is 275 km^2. ■

▶ **Think About It** The area can also be written as 275 square kilometers.

EXAMPLE 7

Marla is making a triangular sail for her boat. The base of the sail must be 8 ft long, and the height must be 12 ft. How many square feet of canvas does she need to make the new sail?

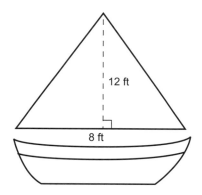

SOLUTION

$A = \dfrac{1}{2}bh$ Use the formula.

$= \dfrac{1}{2} \cdot \mathbf{8} \cdot \mathbf{12}$ Substitute $b = 8$ and $h = 12$.

$= 4 \cdot 12$ Multiply.

$= 48$ Multiply.

Marla needs 48 ft^2 of canvas to make the sail. ■

Finding Missing Lengths

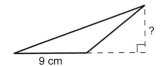

9 cm

A The area of the triangle is 54 cm^2. What is the height of the triangle?

SOLUTION

Substitute the known information into $A = \frac{1}{2}bh$. Solve for h.

$A = \frac{1}{2}bh$ Write the formula.

$54 = \frac{1}{2} \cdot 9 \cdot h$ Substitute 54 for A and 9 for b.

$54 = 4.5h$ Simplify.

$12 = h$ Divide both sides by 4.5.

The height is 12 cm.

B The area of a rectangle is 231 in^2. What is the length of the rectangle if the width is 42 in.?

SOLUTION

Substitute the known information into $A = lw$. Solve for l.

$A = lw$ Write the formula.

$231 = l \cdot 42$ Substitute 231 for A and 42 for w.

$5.5 = l$ Divide both sides by 42.

The length is 5.5 in. ▪

Special Quadrilaterals

A quadrilateral can have zero pairs, one pair, or two pairs of parallel sides.

▶ **Think About It** Arrows are used to indicate parallel lines and segments.

Definitions
A **trapezoid** is a quadrilateral with exactly one pair of parallel sides.
A **parallelogram** is a quadrilateral with two pairs of parallel sides.

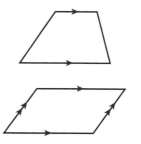

Parallelograms are further classified by their side and angle measures.

Types of Parallelograms

A **rectangle** is a quadrilateral with four right angles.

A **rhombus** is a quadrilateral with four congruent sides.

A **square** is a quadrilateral with four congruent sides and four right angles.

> ▶ **Think About It** The plural of rhombus is rhombi.

All rectangles, rhombi, and squares are also parallelograms.

Classifying Quadrilaterals

EXAMPLE 1

For each figure, write all names that apply: trapezoid, parallelogram, rectangle, rhombus, and square.

A

SOLUTION
Both pairs of sides are parallel, so the figure is a parallelogram. Because all the angles are right angles, it is also a rectangle.

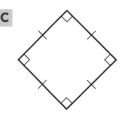

SOLUTION

Only one pair of sides is parallel. The figure is a trapezoid.

C

SOLUTION

All four angles are right angles and all four sides are congruent. The figure is a parallelogram, rectangle, rhombus, and square. ▪

A chart can show how the special quadrilaterals are related.

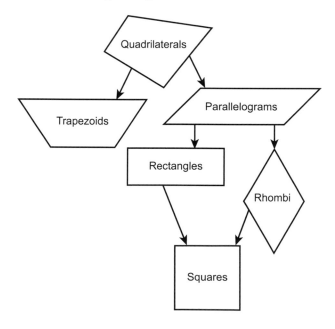

A figure always belongs to a classification above it in the chart, provided they are connected. For example, all parallelograms are quadrilaterals.

A figure will sometimes belong to a classification below it, provided they are connected. For example, a quadrilateral is sometimes a parallelogram.

Figures that are not connected will never belong to the same classification. For example, a parallelogram is never a trapezoid.

> **Think About It** A square can be defined as a rectangle with four congruent sides, or as a rhombus with four right angles.

EXAMPLE 2

Tell if each statement is *always, sometimes,* or *never* true.

A A rectangle is a square.

SOLUTION
Some rectangles are squares, but not all are. Only rectangles with all sides congruent are squares. The statement is *sometimes* true.

B A square is a rectangle.

SOLUTION
Every square is a rectangle because all squares have four right angles. The statement is *always* true.

C A square is a parallelogram.

SOLUTION
A square is always a parallelogram. Both pairs of sides are always parallel, so the statement is *always* true.

D A rhombus is a trapezoid.

SOLUTION
A rhombus always has two pairs of parallel sides, while a trapezoid always has exactly one pair of parallel sides. The statement is *never* true. ■

Using Properties of Parallelograms

Parallelograms have properties that other quadrilaterals do not have.

Properties of Parallelograms

The opposite sides of a parallelogram are congruent. The opposite angles of a parallelogram are congruent.

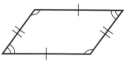

▶ **Think About It** The opposite sides are the parallel sides. The opposite angles do not have a common side.

EXAMPLE 3

AWRT is a parallelogram. Which sides are congruent? Which angles are congruent?

SOLUTION

Opposite sides are congruent: $\overline{AT} \cong \overline{WR}$ and $\overline{WA} \cong \overline{RT}$.

Opposite angles are congruent: $\angle A \cong \angle R$ and $\angle W \cong \angle T$.

▶ **Think About It**
NOTATION $\cong$ means "congruent to"

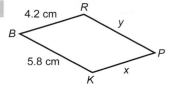

B

Find the values of x and y in the parallelogram.

SOLUTION

Opposite sides of a parallelogram are congruent.

$\overline{BR} \cong \overline{KP}$, so $x = 4.2$ cm.

$\overline{BK} \cong \overline{RP}$, so $y = 5.8$ cm. ■

Areas of Special Quadrilaterals

The formulas for the area of a parallelogram and for a trapezoid are similar to the area formula for a rectangle.

Parallelograms and trapezoids have bases and heights. A **base** is defined to be the bottom side of a geometric figure. The **height** is perpendicular to the base. It is the length of the segment that extends from the base to the opposite side.

Finding the Area of a Parallelogram

Every parallelogram has four bases; each side can be a base. The height depends on which side is used as the base. Heights are sometimes shown outside the parallelogram.

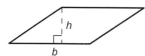  

▶ **Think About It** Any side of a parallelogram can be the base because the parallelogram can be rotated so that any side is on the bottom.

Area of a Parallelogram

The area of a parallelogram with base b and height h is

$$A = bh.$$

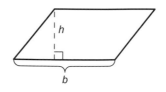

EXAMPLE 1

Find the area of the parallelogram.

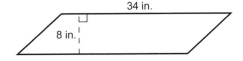

SOLUTION

$A = bh$ Write the formula.

$= 34 \cdot 8$ Substitute 34 for b and 8 for h.

$= 272$ Multiply.

The area is 272 in². ■

Finding the Area of a Trapezoid

A trapezoid has two bases: b_1 and b_2. The parallel sides are always the bases. The height is the length of a segment that joins the bases and forms right angles with them.

Area of a Trapezoid
The area of a trapezoid with bases b_1 and b_2 and height h is $$A = \frac{1}{2}h\left(b_1 + b_2\right).$$ 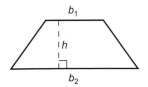

EXAMPLE 2

Find the area of the trapezoid.

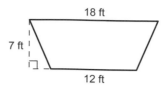

SOLUTION

$A = \frac{1}{2}h(b_1 + b_2)$ Write the formula.

$= \frac{1}{2} \cdot 7 \cdot (18 + 12)$ Substitute 18 for b_1, 12 for b_2 and 7 for h.

$= \frac{1}{2} \cdot 7 \cdot 30$ Simplify inside the parentheses.

$= 105$ Multiply.

The area is 105 ft^2. ■

▶ **Think About It** It does not matter which base is used for b_1 and which is used for b_2.

Finding Missing Lengths

With a known area and some algebra, you can find missing side lengths.

EXAMPLE 3

A The area of a parallelogram is 675 cm^2. What is the height of the parallelogram if its base is 45 cm long?

SOLUTION

Substitute the known information into $A = bh$. Solve for h.

$A = bh$ Write the formula.

$675 = 45 \cdot h$ Substitute 675 for A and 45 for b.

$15 = h$ Divide both sides by 45.

The height is 15 cm.

B The area of the trapezoid is 54 m. Find the unknown base length.

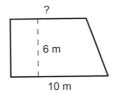

SOLUTION

$A = \frac{1}{2}h(b_1 + b_2)$ Write the formula.

$54 = \frac{1}{2} \cdot 6 \cdot (b_1 + 10)$ Substitute 54 for A, 6 for h, and 10 for one of the bases.

$54 = 3 \cdot (b_1 + 10)$ Multiply on the right.

$18 = b_1 + 10$ Divide both sides by 3.

$8 = b_1$ Subtract 10 from both sides.

The length of the unknown base is 8 m.

CHECK

$$A = \frac{1}{2}h(b_1 + b_2) = \frac{1}{2} \cdot 6 \cdot (8 + 10) = 3 \cdot 18 = 54 \checkmark \blacksquare$$

Problem Solving with Areas of Parallelograms and Trapezoids

You can use the formulas for area of parallelograms and trapezoids to solve real-world problems.

EXAMPLE 4

The Nguyen family is adding a new patio to their backyard. A sketch of the parallelogram-shaped patio is shown. How many square feet of tile will they need to cover the patio?

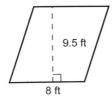

▶ **Q&A**

Q What must be true about the height of a parallelogram?

A The height is perpendicular to the base of the parallelogram.

SOLUTION

Use the formula for area of a parallelogram.

$A = bh$ Write the formula.

$= 8 \cdot 9.5$ Substitute 8 for b and 9.5 for h.

$= 76$ Multiply.

The family will need 76 ft^2 of tile to cover the patio. ■

EXAMPLE 5

Sarah is painting the trapezoid shown onto a wall. One can of paint covers 40 ft^2. How many cans of paint will she need?

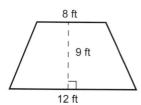

8 ft

9 ft

12 ft

SOLUTION

Use the formula for the area of a trapezoid.

Step 1 Determine the area of what Sarah needs to paint.

$A = \frac{1}{2}h(b_1 + b_2)$ Write the formula.

$= \frac{1}{2} \cdot 9 \cdot (8 + 12)$ Substitute 9 for h and 8 and 12 for the bases.

$= \frac{1}{2} \cdot 9 \cdot 20$ Add inside the parentheses first.

$= \frac{1}{2} \cdot 180$ Multiply.

$= 90$

Sarah will paint 90 ft^2.

> ▶ **Remember** To simplify $\frac{1}{2} \cdot 9 \cdot 20$, you can multiply factors in any order. Multiply 9 by 20 first, since $\frac{1}{2} \cdot 9$ will not give a whole-number product.

Step 2 Determine the number of cans of paint Sarah needs.

$90 = 40 \cdot n$	Here, n is the number of cans of paint.
$90 \div 40 = 40 \cdot n \div 40$	Divide each side by 40.
$2.25 = n$	Divide.

Since she cannot buy a partial can of paint, Sarah will need 3 cans of paint. ■

EXAMPLE 6

Leigh Ann is making a quilt to display at the state fair using pieces that are parallelograms. To make sure all her pieces fit on the fabric, the area of each piece must be 19.5 in^2. The base of each piece is 6.5 in. long. What is the height of each piece?

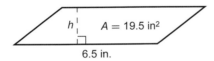

h $A = 19.5$ in²

6.5 in.

SOLUTION
Substitute the known information into $A = bh$. Solve for b.

$A = bh$	Write the formula.
$19.5 = 6.5 \cdot h$	Substitute 19.5 for A and 6.5 for b.
$3 = h$	Divide both sides by 6.5.

Each piece of the quilt must have a height of 3 in. ■

EXAMPLE 7

Marcus is reviewing blueprints for his house. The builder noted the area of one side of the roof, which is a trapezoid, as 390 ft^2, the top length of the roof as 25 ft, and the height as 12 ft. He forgot to label the measurement for the bottom of the roof. What is the missing measurement?

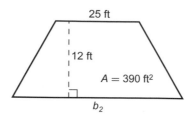

25 ft

12 ft

$A = 390$ ft²

b_2

SOLUTION

Substitute the known information into $A = \frac{1}{2}h(b_1 + b_2)$. Solve for b_2.

$A = \frac{1}{2}h(b_1 + b_2)$ Write the formula.

$390 = \frac{1}{2} \cdot 12 \cdot (25 + b_2)$ Substitute 390 for A, 12 for h, and 25 for one of the bases.

$390 = 6 \cdot (25 + b_2)$ Multiply on the right.

$65 = 25 + b_2$ Divide both sides by 6.

$40 = b_2$ Subtract 25 from both sides.

The length of the bottom of the roof is 40 ft. ■

Application: Painting

EXAMPLE 8

Each wall of a four-sided garden shed is 10 ft long and 8 ft high and has one rhombus-shaped window. The windows are congruent and each has a base of 2 ft and a height of 1.5 ft. The gardener wants to paint the inside of the walls. A can of the paint covers 350 ft²/gal. How many cans of paint will she need for two coats?

▶ **Think About It** Draw a picture of one wall to help you understand the problem.

SOLUTION

Find the area to be painted.

First, find the area that is covered with one coat.

$A = 4lw - 4bh$ Subtract the area of the windows from the area of the walls.

$= 4 \cdot 10 \cdot 8 - 4 \cdot 2 \cdot 1.5$ Substitute values for the variables.

$= 320 - 12$ Multiply.

$= 308$ Subtract.

▶ **Think About It** You can also use $A = 4(lw - bh)$.

She has to cover 308 ft^2 for one coat.

Next, double that amount to find the area covered in two coats.

$2 \times 308 = 616$ Multiply area of one coat by 2.

Divide by 350 to find how many cans of paint she needs.

$616 \div 350 = 1.76$ Divide by 350.

The gardener needs 2 cans of paint. ■

Area of Triangles

If you divide any parallelogram in half, you create two triangles that have equal size.

Bases and Heights of Triangles

Definitions
An **acute** triangle has three acute angles. 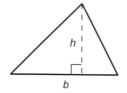
An **obtuse** triangle has one obtuse angle. 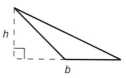
A **right** triangle has one right angle. 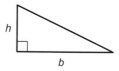

The base of a triangle always forms a right angle with the height.

Think About It Any side of a triangle can be the base. The height will change accordingly.

For every acute triangle, all three heights are inside the triangle.

For every right triangle, two of the heights are sides of the triangle, while one height is inside the triangle.

For every obtuse triangle, two of the heights lie outside the triangle and one lies inside the triangle.

EXAMPLE 1

Find the lengths of the three bases of the triangle and the corresponding height for each base.

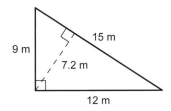

SOLUTION

Find the height for each base.

For $b = 12$ m, $h = 9$ m.

For $b = 9$ m, $h = 12$ m.

For $b = 15$ m, $h = 7.2$ m.

The three bases and corresponding heights for the triangle are 12 m, 9 m; 9 m, 12 m; and 15 m, 7.2 m. ■

Finding the Area of a Triangle

When finding the area of a triangle, express your answer in square units.

▶ **Remember** The area of a triangle with base b and height h is

$$A = \frac{1}{2}bh$$

or

$$A = \frac{bh}{2}.$$

▶ **Think About It** If you can remember that the area of a parallelogram is the product of its base and its height, you can remember that the area of a triangle is one-half that product.

EXAMPLE 2

Find the area of the triangle.

A

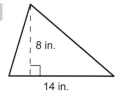

8 in.

14 in.

SOLUTION

$A = \dfrac{bh}{2}$

$= \dfrac{14 \cdot 8}{2}$ Substitute for b and h.

$= \dfrac{112}{2}$ Multiply.

$= 56$ Simplify.

The area is 56 in^2.

B

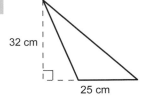

32 cm

25 cm

SOLUTION

$A = \frac{1}{2}bh$

$\quad = \frac{1}{2}(25 \cdot 32)$ Substitute for b and h.

$\quad = \frac{1}{2}(800)$ Multiply inside the parentheses.

$\quad = 400$ Multiply.

The area is 400 cm^2. ■

Application: Sails

EXAMPLE 3

The table shows the dimensions of some triangular sails. Which sail has the greatest area?

Sail Measurements

	Base	Height	Area
Sail 1	11 ft	32 ft	
Sail 2	9 ft	35 ft	
Sail 3	12 ft	30 ft	
Sail 4	10 ft	34 ft	

SOLUTION

Find the area of each sail. Then compare the areas.

$A_1 = \frac{1}{2}b_1h_1 = \frac{1}{2}(11 \cdot 32) = 176$

$A_2 = \frac{1}{2}b_2h_2 = \frac{1}{2}(9 \cdot 35) = 157.5$

$A_3 = \frac{1}{2}b_3h_3 = \frac{1}{2}(12 \cdot 30) = 180$

$A_4 = \frac{1}{2}b_4h_4 = \frac{1}{2}(10 \cdot 34) = 170$

$180 > 176 > 170 > 157.5$

The greatest sail area is 180 ft^2. Sail 3 has the greatest area. ▪

Figures on a Coordinate Plane

Some problems about figures on a coordinate plane will ask you to find missing vertices.

Completing Rectangles and Squares

When the problems are about rectangles and squares, use the fact that opposite sides are parallel.

▶ **Think About It** A horizontal line contains all points with the same y-coordinates. A vertical line contains all points with the same x-coordinates.

EXAMPLE 1

Three vertices of rectangle $ABCD$ are $A\left(-4, 2\right)$, $B\left(3, 2\right)$, and $C\left(3, -3\right)$. Find the coordinates of the fourth vertex.

SOLUTION

Plot the three given points.

Point D will have the same x-coordinate as point A.

Point D will have the same y-coordinate as point C.

The fourth vertex is $D\left(-4, -3\right)$.

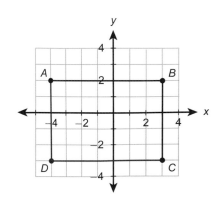

Working with Polygons in the Coordinate Plane

You can use the coordinates of the vertices of a polygon on the coordinate plane to calculate length, perimeter, and area.

EXAMPLE 2

The vertices of triangle ABC are $A(-1, 5)$, $B(-1, -3)$, and $C(6, -3)$. Find the lengths of $\overline{AB}$ and $\overline{BC}$.

SOLUTION

Step 1 Plot the three given points. Connect the points with line segments.

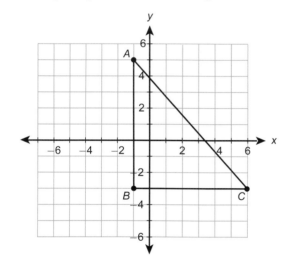

▶ **Think About It** You can count units to find the length of a horizontal or vertical segment.

Step 2 Determine side lengths. Note that A and B have the same x-coordinate and form a vertical line. Points B and C have the same y-coordinate and form a horizontal line.

Find the length of $\overline{AB}$.

A is 5 units from 0 on the x-axis. B is 3 units from 0 on the x-axis. They are $5 + 3 = 8$ units apart.

Find the length of $\overline{BC}$.

B is 1 unit from 0 on the y-axis. C is 6 units from 0 on the y-axis. They are $1 + 6 = 7$ units apart.

Segment $\overline{AB}$ is 8 units long. Segment $\overline{BC}$ is 7 units long. ■

EXAMPLE 3

The vertices of rectangle $LMNP$ are $L(-4, 2)$, $M(-4, -3)$, $N(5, -3)$, and $P(5, 2)$. What are the perimeter and area of the rectangle?

SOLUTION

Step 1 Plot the given points. Connect the points with line segments.

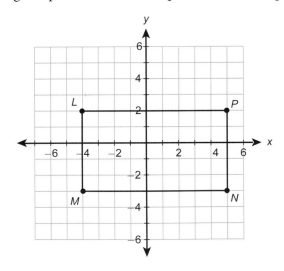

Step 2 Determine side lengths.

Since $\overline{LM}$ is a vertical line, you can count units to find the distance. The x-axis divides the line into parts. The line is $2 + 3 = 5$ units long.

$\overline{MN}$ is a horizontal line, so you can count units to find the distance. The y-axis divides the line into parts. The line is $4 + 5 = 9$ units long.

Step 3 Find the perimeter.

$$P = 2l + 2w = 2(5) + 2(9) = 10 + 18 = 28 \text{ units}$$

Find the area.

$$A = l \bullet w = 5 \bullet 9 = 45 \text{ units}^2 \ \blacksquare$$

Nets of Solids

Some problems about figures on a coordinate plane will ask you to find missing vertices.

Prisms and Pyramids

Prisms and pyramids are two kinds of three-dimensional figures. They have similarities and differences.

Definitions

A **prism** is a three-dimensional figure whose surfaces, called faces, are polygons. At least two faces are parallel and congruent and are called bases. All other faces are rectangles or parallelograms.

A **rectangular prism** has rectangular (or even square) bases, while a **triangular prism** has triangular bases.

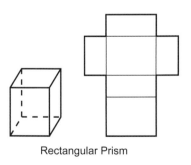

Rectangular Prism

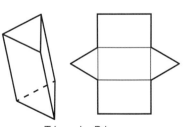

Triangular Prism

Definitions

A **pyramid** is a three-dimensional figure with one base that is a polygon and all other faces (called lateral faces) are triangles that meet at a single vertex.

A **rectangular pyramid** has four triangular faces and a rectangle base. A **triangular pyramid** has a base that is a triangle and three triangular faces.

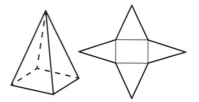

Rectangular Pyramid

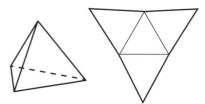

Triangular Pyramid

EXAMPLE 1

Which of these figures are prisms?

Figure 1   Figure 2   Figure 3   Figure 4   Figure 5

SOLUTION

Figure 1 has only one base, so it is not a prism. Figure 2 has two triangular bases that are congruent and parallel, so it is a prism. Figure 3 has only one base, so it is not a prism. Figure 4 does not have polygon faces or a base, so it is not a prism. Figure 5 has two rectangular bases that are congruent and parallel, so it is a prism.

Figures 2 and 5 are prisms. ■

EXAMPLE 2

Compare and contrast the two figures.

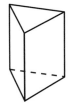

Figure 1   Figure 2

SOLUTION

Both figures are three-dimensional and have a triangular base.

Figure 1 has one base, but Figure 2 has two bases.

Figure 2 has parallel bases, but Figure 1 does not.

Figure 1 has triangle faces, but Figure 2 has rectangle faces.

Figure 1 is a triangular pyramid and Figure 2 is a triangular prism. ■

Using Nets to Represent Solids

Definition
The **net** of a solid figure is a pattern of polygons that can be folded to form that solid figure.

To match a net to a solid figure, compare the polygons that make up the net to the faces of the solid figure.

▶ **Remember** A polygon is a closed figure formed by three or more line segments in a plane, where each line segment intersects two other line segments at their endpoints only.

EXAMPLE 3

Match the net to the solid figure.

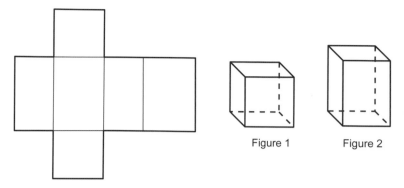

Figure 1   Figure 2

SOLUTION

The net is made up of four rectangles and two squares.

Figure 1 is a cube, so its faces are all squares. The faces do not match the polygons in the net.

Figure 2 is a rectangular prism, and its faces are four rectangles and two squares. The faces match the polygons in the net.

The net can be folded into Figure 2. ■

EXAMPLE 4

Match the solid figure to the net.

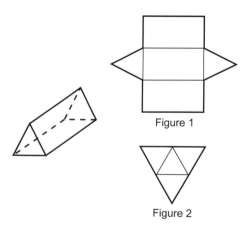

Figure 1

Figure 2

SOLUTION

The given solid has two triangular bases and three rectangular sides.

Figure 1 shows a net made up of two triangles and three rectangles. This net is for a triangular prism.

Figure 2 shows a net made up of four triangles. This net is for a triangular pyramid.

The prism matches Figure 1. ■

Using Nets to Solve Problems

You can draw a net of a solid figure to help solve a problem about the figure.

EXAMPLE 5

Solve. Use the net of the pyramid.

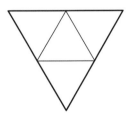

A What is the surface area of a triangular pyramid that has faces with areas of 5 cm^2 each?

SOLUTION
There are four faces.

$4 \cdot 5 = 20$ Multiply the area of one face by the number of faces.

The surface area is 20 cm^2.

B What is the area of one face of a triangular pyramid if the pyramid's total surface area is 24 mm^2?

SOLUTION

$24 \div 4 = 6$ Divide the surface area by the number of faces.

The area of one face is 6 mm^2. ■

EXAMPLE 6

Use the net of the rectangular prism. The area of each face is labeled. What is the surface area of the prism?

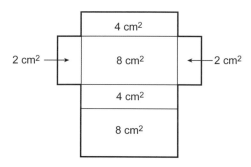

▶ **Think About It** To find the surface area of a solid, find the area of each face and then add.

SOLUTION

There are six faces.

Two faces have an area of 2 cm^2: $2 \cdot 2 = 4$.

Two faces have an area of 4 cm^2: $2 \cdot 4 = 8$.

Two faces have an area of 8 cm^2: $2 \cdot 8 = 16$.

The surface area is $4 + 8 + 16 = 28$ cm^2. ■

Problem Solving: Surface Area

Surface area is the sum of the areas of all the faces of a solid. You can use nets to help you solve problems about surface area.

EXAMPLE 7

A package of fruit snacks is shaped like a square pyramid. The base is 5 in. on each side. The height of each triangle face is 6 in. What is the surface area? Draw a net to help you.

SOLUTION

▶ **Remember** The formula for area of a triangle is $A = \frac{1}{2}bh$.

Draw a net.

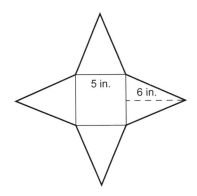

$A = l \cdot w = 5 \cdot 5 = 25$ Find the area of the square base.

$A = \frac{1}{2}bh = \frac{1}{2}(5 \cdot 6) = \frac{1}{2} \cdot 30 = 15$ Find the area of each triangle face.

$4 \cdot 15 = 60$ Since there are 4 triangle faces, multiply 4 by 15.

$25 + 60 = 85$ Add the areas.

The surface area of the package is 85 in^2. ▪

EXAMPLE 8

Dave is making a special box for his father using curly maple wood shaped like a rectangular prism. The box will have a length of 20 cm, a width of 16 cm, and a height of 16 cm. What will be the surface area of the box? Draw a net to help you.

SOLUTION

Find the area of each base.

Draw a net.

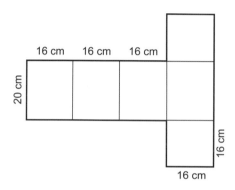

$A = l \cdot w = 20 \cdot 16 = 320$	There are 4 faces that are 20 cm by 16 cm. Find the area of 1 face.
$4 \cdot 320 = 1280$	Since there are 4 faces, multiply by 4.
$A = l \cdot w = 16 \cdot 16 = 256$	There are 2 faces that are 16 cm by 16 cm. Find the area of 1 face.
$2 \cdot 256 = 512$	Since there are 2 faces, multiply by 2.
$1280 + 512 = 1792$	Add the areas.

The surface area of the box will be 1792 cm^2. ∎

Volume

Volume describes the space inside a solid.

Using Cubes to Find the Volume

Definition

The **volume** of a solid is the amount of space taken up by a three-dimensional object. Volume is measured in cubic units.

Volume is the number of unit cubes that fit inside a solid.

How to Find the Volume of a Prism with Fractional Edge Lengths

Step 1 Determine the size of unit cubes to use.

Step 2 Find the number of fractional unit cubes it takes to fill the prism.

Step 3 Divide the total number of cubes in the prism by the number of cubes in a unit cube.

EXAMPLE 1

Use fractional unit cubes to determine the volume of the cube.

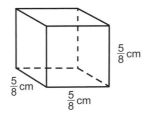

$\frac{5}{8}$ cm

$\frac{5}{8}$ cm

$\frac{5}{8}$ cm

A This cube is smaller than a unit cube. Each side length is shorter than 1 cm. Fill it with fractional unit cubes. Determine the edge length of cubes that can be used to pack the solid.

SOLUTION

Try different cubes to find one that will fill all the edges of the solid.

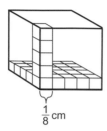

$\frac{1}{8}$ cm

Each edge of the solid can be filled with cubes that have edge lengths of $\frac{1}{8}$ cm.

B Find the number of $\frac{1}{8}$ cm cubes that fill one layer of the solid.

> ▶ **Q&A**
>
>   **Q** What is one way to find the total number of fractional unit cubes that fill the prism?
>
>   **A** Find the number of cubes in the bottom layer, and multiply by the number of layers.

SOLUTION

Fill the bottom layer of the solid with $\frac{1}{8}$ cm cubes.

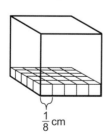

$\frac{1}{8}$ cm

Each layer of the cube can be filled with 25 cubes with edge lengths of $\frac{1}{8}$ cm.

C Find the volume of the solid.

> ▶ **Think About It** It would take $8 \cdot 8 \cdot 8$ (or 512) fractional cubes to fill a unit cube. So divide the total number of fractional unit cubes in this cube by 512 to find the volume of the cube.

SOLUTION

5×25 There are 5 layers of 25 fractional cubes in the cube.

$= 125$ Multiply. There are 125 fractional unit cubes in the cube.

$= \dfrac{125}{512}$ Divide to find the volume.

The volume of the prism is $\dfrac{125}{512}$ cm^3. ■

EXAMPLE 2

Use fractional unit cubes to determine the volume of the rectangular prism.

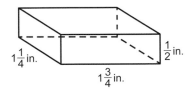

$1\frac{1}{4}$ in. $1\frac{3}{4}$ in. $\frac{1}{2}$ in.

A Determine the edge length of cubes that can be used to pack the solid.

SOLUTION

Try different cubes to find one that will fill all the edges of the solid without gaps or overlaps.

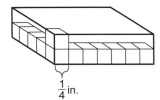

$\frac{1}{4}$ in.

Each edge of the solid can be filled with cubes that have edge lengths of $\frac{1}{4}$ in.

B Find the number of unit cubes it takes to fill 1 layer of the solid.

SOLUTION

Fill the bottom layer of the solid with $\frac{1}{4}$ in. cubes.

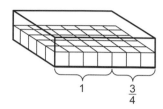

1     $\frac{3}{4}$

Each layer of the cube can be filled with 35 fractional cubes.

C Find the volume of the solid.

▶ **Think About It** Each edge of a unit cube can fit 4 cubes with edge lengths of $\frac{1}{4}$ in. So a 1 in. cube can fit $4 \cdot 4 \cdot 4 = 64$ fractional unit cubes.

SOLUTION

$2 \cdot 35$	There are 2 layers of 35 cubes.
$= 70$	Multiply. It takes 70 fractional unit cubes $\left(\text{of edge length } \frac{1}{4}\right)$ to fill the prism.
$70 \div 64$	There are $4 \cdot 4 \cdot 4 = 64$ fractional cubes in a 1 in. cube.
$= \dfrac{70}{64}$	Divide to find the volume.
$= \dfrac{35}{32} = 1\dfrac{3}{32}$	Simplify.

The volume of the prism is $1\frac{3}{32}$ in^3. ▪

Using a Formula to Find the Volume

Volume of a Rectanglular Prism

The volume of a rectangular prism is

$$V = lwh,$$

where l = length, w = width, and h = height.

You can use a formula to find the volume of a rectangular prism.

EXAMPLE 3

Find the volume of the rectangular prism.

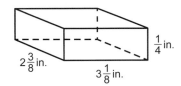

SOLUTION

$V = lwh$ Use the formula to find the volume.

$= 3\frac{1}{8} \cdot 2\frac{3}{8} \cdot \frac{1}{4}$ Substitute values for length, width, and height.

$= \frac{25}{8} \cdot \frac{19}{8} \cdot \frac{1}{4}$ Rewrite the mixed numbers as improper fractions.

$= \frac{475}{256}$ Multiply numerators. Multiply denominators.

$= 1\frac{219}{256}$ Simplify.

The volume of the prism is $1\frac{219}{256}$ in^3. ∎

▶ **Remember** Divide out common factors before multiplying fractions, if possible.

EXAMPLE 4

The volume of the rectangular prism shown is $35\frac{7}{16}$ yd^3. Find the height of the prism.

SOLUTION

$V = lwh$ Use the formula to find the height.

$35\frac{7}{16} = 3\frac{1}{2} \cdot 4\frac{1}{2} \cdot h$ Substitute values for volume, length, and width.

$\frac{567}{16} = \frac{7}{2} \cdot \frac{9}{2} \cdot h$ Rewrite mixed numbers as improper fractions.

$\frac{567}{16} = \frac{63}{4} \cdot h$ Multiply the fractions on the right side.

$\frac{9}{4} = h$ Divide by $\frac{63}{4}$ to solve for h.

$2\frac{1}{4} = h$ Simplify.

The height of the prism is $2\frac{1}{4}$ yd. ■

▶ **Remember** When dividing fractions, multiply by the reciprocal.

Problem Solving: Using Fractional Dimensions to Find the Volume

You can use the formula for volume of rectangular prisms to solve real-world problems.

EXAMPLE 5

A gym is building a new lap pool and needs to plan how much water it needs to operate the pool. The pool is 50 m long, $2\frac{1}{2}$ m wide, and $6\frac{1}{4}$ m deep. What is the volume of the new pool?

SOLUTION

$V = lwh$ Use the formula to find the volume.

$= 50 \cdot 2\frac{1}{2} \cdot 6\frac{1}{4}$ Substitute values for length, width, and height.

$= \frac{50}{1} \cdot \frac{5}{2} \cdot \frac{25}{4}$ Rewrite mixed numbers as improper fractions.

$= \frac{\overset{25}{\cancel{50}}}{1} \cdot \frac{5}{\underset{1}{\cancel{2}}} \cdot \frac{25}{4}$ Divide 50 and 2 by 2.

$= \frac{3125}{4}$ Multiply.

$= 781\frac{1}{4}$ Simplify.

The volume of the new pool will be $781\frac{1}{4}$ m^3. ∎

EXAMPLE 6

A store needs to ship $151\frac{15}{16}$ ft^3 of goods to another store. All the standard pallets in the warehouse have footprints $5\frac{1}{2}$ ft long by $4\frac{1}{4}$ ft wide. How tall would the box need to be in order to ship the goods?

SOLUTION

$V = lwh$ Use the formula to find the height.

$151\frac{15}{16} = 5\frac{1}{2} \cdot 4\frac{1}{4} \cdot h$ Substitute values.

$\frac{2431}{16} = \frac{11}{2} \cdot \frac{17}{4} \cdot h$ Rewrite mixed numbers as improper fractions.

$\frac{2431}{16} = \frac{187}{8} \cdot h$ Multiply on the right.

$\frac{13}{2} = h$ Solve for h.

$6\frac{1}{2} = h$ Simplify.

The box must be at least $6\frac{1}{2}$ ft tall. ∎

Volumes of Prisms

You know how to use the formula $V = lwh$ for volume of a prism. There is another formula that works for finding volume of prisms.

Finding the Volume of a Rectangular Prism

Definition

A **prism** is a three-dimensional figure whose surfaces, called faces, are polygons. At least two faces are parallel and congruent and are called bases. All other faces are rectangles or parallelograms.

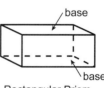

Rectangular Prism

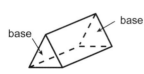

Triangular Prism

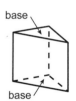

Triangular Prism

▶ **Think About It** Any pair of opposite faces in a rectangular prism can be considered its bases.

Volume of a Prism

The volume of a prism with a base area of B and a height of h is
$$V = Bh.$$

▶ Think About It

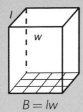

$B = lw$

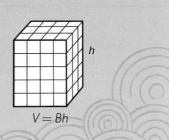

$V = Bh$

To use the formula to find the volume of a rectangular prism, first find the area of one of its bases, and then multiply that area by the prism's height.

EXAMPLE 1

Find the volume of the rectangular prism.

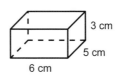

3 cm
5 cm
6 cm

▶ **Remember** The area of a rectangle with length l and width w is

$$A = lw.$$

SOLUTION

$B = \textbf{\textit{lw}}$	Find the area of the base.
$= \textbf{6} \cdot \textbf{5}$	Substitute 6 for l and 5 for w.
$= 30$	Multiply.
$V = \textbf{\textit{Bh}}$	
$= \textbf{30} \cdot \textbf{3}$	Substitute 30 for B and 3 for h.
$= 90$	Multiply.

The volume of the rectangular prism is 90 cm^3. ■

EXAMPLE 2

The volume of the prism is 30 in^3. What is the length?

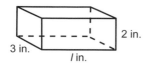

SOLUTION

$V = Bh$	Use the formula for volume of a prism.
$V = lw \cdot h$	Use lw instead of B.
$30 = l \cdot 3 \cdot 2$	Substitute 30 for volume, 3 for width, and 2 for height.
$30 = l \cdot 6$	Simplify.
$5 = l$	Divide both sides by 6.

The length of the rectangular prism is 5 in. ■

EXAMPLE 3

Mr. George needs to fill his planter with dirt. How many cubic feet of dirt does he need to buy?

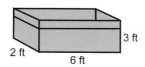

SOLUTION

$B = lw$	Find the area of the base.
$= 6 \cdot 2$	Substitute.
$= 12$	Multiply.
$V = Bh$	
$= 12 \cdot 3$	Substitute 12 for B and 3 for h.
$= 36$	Multiply.

Mr. George needs 36 ft^3 of dirt. ■

EXAMPLE 4

A shipping company must ship 2880 ft^2 of material across the country. All of the shipping containers used by the company are 8 ft long and 9 ft high. How wide must the containers be in order to fit the materials?

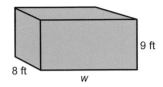

SOLUTION

$V = Bh$	Use the formula for volume of a prism.
$V = lw \cdot h$	Use lw instead of B.
$2880 = 8 \cdot w \cdot 9$	Substitute values for volume, length, and height.
$2880 = w \cdot 72$	Simplify.
$40 = w$	Divide both sides by 72.

The width of the shipping containers must be 40 ft. ▪

Statistical Graphs

Cyclists can track their performance to ensure they are peaking at the right time. Why would athletes use graphs to represent their performance data? A graph paints a picture of trends and patterns.

Statistical Questions

Statistical questions are used to collect data that show variability within a population.

Identifying and Writing Statistical Questions

When a statistical question is asked, a variety of responses are possible. One example of a statistical question is "How many sisters do each of my classmates have?" Each person who answers the question could have a different answer. However, the question "How many students are on the soccer team?" would only have one answer. Therefore, it is not a statistical question. When a statistical question is asked, a list of varying responses must be possible.

EXAMPLE 1

Decide whether the example asks a statistical question.

A How many books did Karen check out at the library?

SOLUTION
This question is not a statistical question because there is only one possible response.

B How many miles do the sixth-grade students in Villa Grove live from the library?

SOLUTION
This question is a statistical question because not all the students would live the same number of miles from the library. The responses will vary.

C How many songs does a teenager download per month?

SOLUTION
This question is a statistical question because the responses should vary, given each teenager surveyed.

> ▶ **Remember** Statistical questions can be used to collect categorical data or numerical data.

D What types of flowers grow well in the southern United States?

SOLUTION
This question is a statistical question because there is more than one type of flower that grows well in the southern United States. ▪

EXAMPLE 2

Suppose you wanted to learn more about the sleeping habits of the children in your neighborhood. Write a statistical question you could use to learn about their sleeping habits.

SOLUTION
A possible question is "How many hours of sleep do the children in my neighborhood typically get each night?" ▪

EXAMPLE 3

Write a statistical question that can be used to learn about physical characteristics of owls.

SOLUTION
A possible question is "What is the wingspan of an owl?" ▪

More Statistical Graphs

Different types of graphs can be used to display sets of data differently.

Interpreting Statistical Graphs

Definitions

A **bar graph** uses bars to display data.

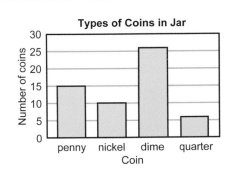

A **line plot** uses dots or Xs to display individual data values with a number line.

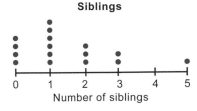

A **line graph** displays data values as a series of points connected by straight line segments.

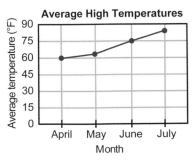

EXAMPLE 1

Use the graphs in the Definitions box to answer the questions.

A How many more pennies than nickels are shown in the bar graph?

SOLUTION
Read the bar for each coin and subtract: $15 - 10 = 5$.

There are 5 more pennies than nickels.

B According to the line plot, what is the ratio of the number of people with exactly 2 siblings to those with just 1 sibling?

SOLUTION
There are 3 people with 2 siblings and 6 people with 1 sibling.

The ratio is $\frac{3}{6}$.

C According to the line graph, what was the temperature difference between April and June?

SOLUTION
temperature in April, 60°F; temperature in June, 75°F

Subtract: $75 - 60 = 15$.

The temperature was 15°F higher in June. ■

Selecting Statistical Graphs

Definitions
Discrete data have distinct intervals between any values. No intermediate values are possible. Examples: colors, shoe sizes, and ages
Continuous data can be any value within a range. Examples: temperature, time, and weight

> ▶ **Think About It** Think about the data set you are trying to represent with a graph. You should use bar graphs and line plots to represent discrete data. You should use line graphs to represent continuous data.

EXAMPLE 2

Explain which type of graph would best display the data.

A town residents' votes for each of four possible new park sites

SOLUTION
Vote numbers are discrete data, best shown in a bar graph or line plot. Bar graphs display larger numbers of data values better.

A bar graph would display the discrete data best.

B heights of a sunflower recorded each week for a month

SOLUTION
Height data are continuous. A line graph displays continuous data best.

A line graph would display the continuous height data best.

C numbers of books read by 10 people over the summer

SOLUTION
Numbers of books are discrete data, so a bar graph or line plot would work best. Line plots display smaller numbers of numeric data values better.

A line plot would display the discrete data best. ▪

Line Plots

When you understand the shape of a data set, you can better see how each data value relates to the whole.

Creating a Line Plot

In the NCAA Women's Soccer tournament, the final game determines the champion. The table shows the number of goals scored in each championship game since the tournament began in 1982 through 2010.

Year	Goals	Year	Goals
1982	1	1997	2
1983	4	1998	1
1984	2	1999	2
1985	2	2000	3
1986	2	2001	1
1987	1	2002	3
1988	5	2003	6
1989	2	2004	2
1990	6	2005	4
1991	4	2006	3
1992	10	2007	2
1993	6	2008	3
1994	5	2009	1
1995	1	2010	1
1996	1		

NCAA 2016

A **line plot** can help you see the shape of the data.

For the soccer final data, the line plot looks like this.

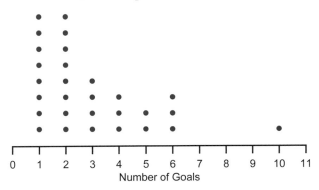

Interpreting a Line Plot

You can tell quite a bit from the line plot displaying the soccer data. For instance,

- Would a total of only 2 goals be unusual? Not at all. In most games, either 1 or 2 goals were scored.

- In how many games were more than 4 goals scored? There were 6 games in which more than 4 goals were scored (that's about 21% of the time).

- Would a total of 7 goals be a lot for a final? Yes, it would. Only once was more than 6 goals scored. So any value more than 6 would be pretty rare.

EXAMPLE

During its growth period, bamboo can grow up to 4 in. in a day. The data show the growth of 16 bamboo plants in a day, in inches.

$$2\tfrac{1}{2}, 4, 3, 2, 3, 2\tfrac{1}{2}, 2, 1\tfrac{3}{4}, 1, 2, 3, 1\tfrac{1}{2}, 3\tfrac{1}{2}, 2\tfrac{3}{4}, 2\tfrac{3}{4}, 3$$

A Make a line plot for these data.

SOLUTION

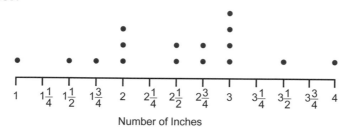

Use the line plot to answer the questions.

B What are the lengths of the bamboo plants that grew between 2 and 3 in.? What is the combined growth of these plants?

SOLUTION

Find the lengths of the bamboo plants that grew between 2 and 3 in. and add them.

$$2\tfrac{1}{2} + 2\tfrac{1}{2} + 2\tfrac{3}{4} + 2\tfrac{3}{4} = 2 + 2 + 2 + 2 + \tfrac{1}{2} + \tfrac{1}{2} + \tfrac{3}{4} + \tfrac{3}{4}$$

$$= 8 + \tfrac{2}{4} + \tfrac{2}{4} + \tfrac{3}{4} + \tfrac{3}{4}$$

$$= 8 + \tfrac{10}{4}$$

$$= 8 + 2\tfrac{2}{4}$$

$$= 8 + 2\tfrac{1}{2}$$

$$= 10\tfrac{1}{2} \text{ in.}$$

C What are the lengths of the three bamboo plants that grew the least? What is the total growth for these three plants?

SOLUTION
Find the three least values and add them.

$$1 + 1\frac{1}{2} + 1\frac{3}{4} = 1 + 1 + 1 + \frac{1}{2} + \frac{3}{4}$$

$$= 3 + \frac{2}{4} + \frac{3}{4}$$

$$= 3 + \frac{5}{4}$$

$$= 3 + 1\frac{1}{4}$$

$$= 4\frac{1}{4} \text{ in.} \blacksquare$$

Distribution Shapes

When looking at a line plot, the shape of the data is called the **distribution** of the data. There are many different possible shapes for a distribution of data, but there are three characteristics of shapes that we often look for.

Symmetrical A data set has a symmetrical distribution if the values below the median are approximately a mirror image of those above the median. In a symmetrical data set, the mean and median are generally pretty close to each other.

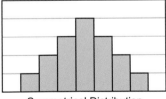
Symmetrical Distribution

Skewed Left A data set is skewed left if the frequency of data is clustered at the higher end of the distribution. In a graph, the left tail of a left-skewed data set is longer than the right tail.

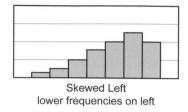

Skewed Left
lower frequencies on left

Skewed Right A data set is skewed right if the frequency of data is clustered at the lower end of the distribution. In a graph, the right tail of a right-skewed data set is longer than the left tail.

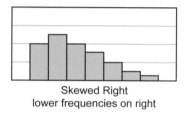

Skewed Right
lower frequencies on right

Gaps and Outliers

Definitions

A line plot has a **gap** when there are no data values for a certain number and when there are data values for numbers on either side.

An **outlier** is a data value that is either much greater or much less than most of the other data values.

It is easy to spot a gap in a line plot because it looks like an empty spot between data values.

There is always a gap between an outlier and the rest of the data set. Outliers can be identified easily on a line plot because they are either far to the right or far to the left of the other data values. There are methods for calculating outliers, but for now, we'll identify outliers visually.

Histograms

You can use a graph to display the numbers of data points that fall within different intervals.

Frequency Tables

One way to organize data is to make a frequency table.

Definition
A **frequency table** shows all values in a data set and how many times each value occurs.

The data values are typically reported in a frequency table within intervals. Each interval needs to be the same size, or range, and there should be no gaps between the intervals. The size and number of intervals will vary based on the values in the data set.

EXAMPLE 1

Create a frequency table for the data set, which shows number of sit-ups in 1 minute.

45, 30, 23, 21, 18, 28, 42, 29, 29, 41, 20, 36, 41, 33, 53, 25, 52, 36, 30, 43

SOLUTION

Step 1 Select reasonable intervals for the data. Use 8 intervals for this data set.

Step 2 Set up intervals of equal size. The least data value is 18, and the greatest data value is 53. Use these intervals: 15–19, 20–24, 25–29, 30–34, 35–39, 40–44, 45–49, and 50–54. Each interval has 5 numbers.

Step 3 Make the frequency table. The frequency for each interval is the number of times the data values occur in that interval.

Interval	Frequency
15–19	1
20–24	3
25–29	4
30–34	3
35–39	2
40–44	4
45–49	1
50–54	2

Drawing Histograms

Definition

A **histogram** is a bar graph that displays the frequency of data values that occur within certain intervals. The height of each bar on a histogram gives the frequency for that bar's interval.

▶ **Think About It** The bars in a histogram touch each other because there are no gaps in the intervals of the data.

Determine the equal-sized numerical intervals you will use, and then find the number of data values that fall within each interval. Be sure to use consecutive intervals, without any gaps. Draw a bar for each interval to show that number.

EXAMPLE 2

Draw a histogram to represent daily rainfall amounts in June, in centimeters.

0, 1, 2, 0, 0, 2, 6, 3, 4, 1, 0, 1, 0, 0, 2, 4, 3, 2, 5, 1, 1, 0, 1, 5, 0, 2, 0, 3, 7, 0

SOLUTION
Select reasonable intervals for the data. The data go from 0 to 7. Use intervals of 0–1, 2–3, 4–5, and 6–7. Count the number of data values in each interval.

0–1, 16 data values
2–3, 8 data values
4–5, 4 data values
6–7, 2 data values

Draw and label the axes. Then draw a bar above each interval.

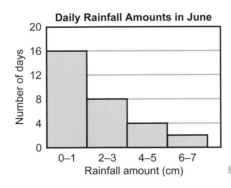

Interpreting Histograms

Read data from a histogram by looking at the heights of the bars and the interval for each.

EXAMPLE 3

Solve using the histograms that show heights of basketball players.

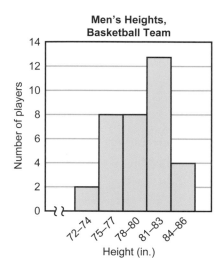
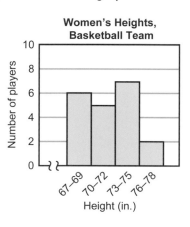

▶ **Think About It** Because data are shown only for intervals, histograms do not show specific data values. You can't tell from the men's histogram, for example, how many players are exactly 82 in. tall.

A How many men players are shorter than 81 in.?

SOLUTION

Add the values for the intervals with heights less than 81 in.

$$2 + 8 + 8 = 18$$

There are 18 men players shorter than 81 in.

B How many women players are 73 in. or taller?

SOLUTION

Add the values for the intervals with heights greater than or equal to 73 in.

$$7 + 2 = 9$$

There are 9 women players who are 73 in. or taller.

C How many men players are as tall as or taller than the tallest woman player?

> ▶ **Think About It** In Example 3C, the greatest height interval for women players is 76–78 in., so you know that the tallest woman is at least 76 in. tall, and at most 78 in. tall.

SOLUTION

Look at the intervals. The tallest woman player could be 78 in. The intervals on the men's graph 78 in. and greater are 78–80, 81–83, and 84–86.

$$8 + 13 + 4 = 25$$

There are 25 men players as tall as or taller than the tallest woman player, if you assume the tallest woman player is 78 in. ■

Stem-and-Leaf Plots

You don't need fancy bar graphs or histograms to see the shape of a data set. Even a simple, but elegant, listing of data can show you the shape.

Interpreting a Stem-and-Leaf Plot

There are earthquakes every day, all over the world. Here is a plot showing magnitudes on the Richter scale of earthquakes detected in various parts of the world on February 14, 2011.

> ▶ **Think About It** On February 14, 2011, the earthquake with the greatest magnitude occurred in the Pacific Ocean about 300 km southwest of Santiago, Chile.

From the stem-and-leaf plot, you can see many things.

```
2 | 1 8
3 | 1 3 3 8 9 9
4 | 4 5 5 5 8 9 9
5 | 0 2 2
6 | 6
```
Key: 2 | 1 means 2.1

- There were four earthquakes that registered 5.0 or higher.
- The strongest earthquake registered 6.6.

To count the number of data values in the data set, just count the number of leaves. In this case, there are 19 data values. It's also easy to list the data values in order.

2.1, 2.8, 3.1, 3.3, 3.3, 3.8, 3.9, 3.9, 4.4, 4.5, 4.5, 4.5, 4.8, 4.9, 4.9, 5.0, 5.2, 5.2, 6.6

If you look at the stem-and-leaf plot sideways, you can see it as a simple histogram, where the categories are defined by the stems. This is a quick way to see the shape of a data set. In this case, the distribution is rather symmetrical.

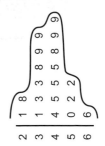

Creating a Stem-and-Leaf Plot

On February 7, 2011, earthquakes with the following magnitudes were detected:

6.4, 4.7, 4.5, 4.5, 4.4, 4.9, 4.7, 2.7, 5.3, 4.2, 4.7, 2.5, 4.3

How to Create a Stem-and-Leaf Plot
Step 1 Arrange the data in increasing order.
Step 2 Draw a vertical line to separate stems from leaves.
Step 3 Write your stems down one side of the line.
Step 4 Write each leaf in increasing order on the right side of the line, and include a key.
Step 5 Count your leaves to ensure you have the right number.

Here are the steps for creating a stem-and-leaf plot for the February 7 data.

Step 1 Arrange the data in increasing order.

2.5, 2.7, 4.2, 4.3, 4.4, 4.5, 4.5, 4.7, 4.7, 4.7, 4.9, 5.3, 6.4

Step 2–4 Draw a vertical line, and then write your stems in order. Finally write each leaf to the right in increasing order.

Step 5 Count the leaves. There are 13 leaves in the plot, and there are 13 data values in the original data set. No data values were skipped.

```
2 | 5 7
3 |
4 | 2 3 4 5 5 7 7 7 9
5 | 3
6 | 4
```

Key: 4 | 5 means 4.5

Double Stem-and-Leaf Plots

You can also combine the data into a single plot known as a double stem-and-leaf plot. When presented this way, you can see the stems straight down the middle with one set of leaves going to the left and the other going to the right.

February 7		February 14
7 5	2	1 8
	3	1 3 3 8 9 9
9 7 7 7 5 5 4 3 2	4	4 5 5 5 8 9 9
3	5	0 2 2
4	6	6

Key: 6 | 2 means 6.2

How would you describe the differences between these two sets of data?

- Both sets of data are rather symmetrical.

- The data for February 7 has a gap when the stem is 3, making 2.5 and 2.7 possible outliers.

> **Remember** An outlier is an extreme value that is far from the rest of the values in a data set.

Box-and-Whisker Plots

Box-and-whisker plots allow you to interpret different things about a set of data.

Interpreting a Box-and-Whisker Plot

Definitions

Quartiles are any of the three values that separate an ordered data set into four equal parts; a quartile also refers to the entire set of data in any quarter of the data, such as all the data between Q_2 and Q_3.

A **box-and-whisker plot** shows the distribution or spread of data; it uses the minimum, the maximum, and the three quartiles of the data to split the data into four quarters, or quartiles, of data.

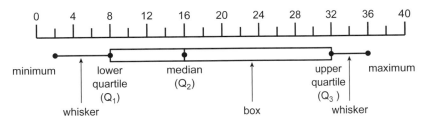

The median of the lower half of the data is the first, or lower, quartile (Q_1). The median of the data is the second quartile (Q_2). The median of the upper half of the data is the third, or upper, quartile (Q_3).

EXAMPLE 1

A What are the highest, lowest, and median test scores? What is the range of each of the four quarters of data?

Test

62 64 66 68 70 72 74 76 78 80 82 84 86 88 90 92 94 96 98 100

SOLUTION

Interpret the box-and-whisker plot.

The maximum is 100, the minimum is 68, and the median is 86.

- first quarter: $78 - 68 = 10$
- second quarter: $86 - 78 = 8$
- third quarter: $91 - 86 = 5$
- fourth quarter: $100 - 91 = 9$

The highest test score is 100, the lowest is 68, and the median is 86. The first-quarter range is 10, the second-quarter range is 8, the third-quarter range is 5, and the fourth-quarter range is 9.

B The box-and-whisker plot was made using the ages of 100 people. In which quarters are the data most concentrated and least concentrated?

Ages of People

42 44 46 48 50 52 54 56 58 60 62 64 66 68 70

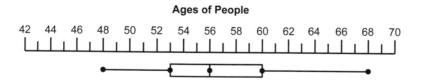

SOLUTION

The lower quartile and median are closest together, indicating data are closest together in the second quarter.

The upper quartile and maximum are furthest apart, indicating data are the most spread out in the fourth quarter.

The second quarter has the most-concentrated data and the fourth quarter has the least-concentrated data. ■

Making a Box-and-Whisker Plot

Find the lower and upper extremes and the quartiles to help you make a box-and-whisker plot.

EXAMPLE 2

Use the data to make a box-and-whisker plot.

```
2 | 3
3 | 2  2  6  8
4 | 0  1  3  4  9
```
Key: 3|6 means 36

SOLUTION

Find the minimum, the maximum, and the quartiles. Then draw the number line, points, box, and whiskers.

minimum: 23

maximum: 49

median: $\dfrac{38 + 40}{2} = 39$

first quartile: 32 (median of lower half of data)

third quartile: 43 (median of upper half of data)

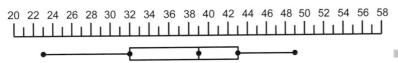

▶ **Think About It** When drawing the number line, start with a value less than the minimum and a value greater than the maximum. Use a ruler to help draw the number line, box, and whiskers.

Measures of Center and Spread

Topic List

Every sea urchin can be described. Each one has color, mass, and age. The language and tools of statistics help describe all sorts of data.

Measures of Center

Measures of center, like mean and median, can help summarize a set of data.

Finding Mean, Median, and Mode

Definition

A **stem-and-leaf plot** is a graph used to organize and display data.

```
0 | 0  1  5          This line represents 0, 1, and 5.
1 | 5  6  7  7  8     This line represents 15, 16, 17, 17, and 18.
2 | 0  2  8  9        This line represents 20, 22, 28, and 29.
3 | 4  4  6           This line represents 34, 34, and 36.
Key: 2|2 means 22
```

Data shown in a table or stem-and-leaf plot can make it easier to calculate the mean, median, and mode.

EXAMPLE 1

Find the mean, median, and mode of the test scores shown in the stem-and-leaf plot.

```
7 | 9  9
8 | 2  4  6  8  9
9 | 0  1  2
Key: 8|2 means 82
```

SOLUTION

Use the stem-and-leaf plot.

mean: $\dfrac{79 + 79 + 82 + 84 + 86 + 88 + 89 + 90 + 91 + 92}{10} = \dfrac{860}{10} = 86$

median: There are 10 test scores. The median is the average of the fifth and sixth test scores.

$$\frac{86 + 88}{2} = \frac{174}{2} = 87$$

mode: The number 79 occurs more than any other number.

The mean is 86, the median is 87, and the mode is 79. ■

> **Remember** The mean is the sum of the values in a data set divided by the number of values.
>
> The median is the middle value in a data set, or the average of the two middle numbers.
>
> The mode is the value or values that appear most often in a data set.

Weighted Average

In a weighted average, some data values will contribute more to the average than others.

EXAMPLE 2

Eliza had a summer job gardening. She earned $65 each week for 5 wk, $78 each week for 3 wk, and $40 each week for 2 wk. What was her average weekly pay?

SOLUTION

Be sure to include Eliza's earnings for each week that she worked.

$$\frac{(65 \cdot 5) + (78 \cdot 3) + (40 \cdot 2)}{10} = \frac{639}{10}$$
$$= 63.9$$

Eliza's average weekly pay was $63.90. ■

▶ **Q&A**

Q Why can't you just add $65 + 78 + 40$, and then divide by 3?

A Think of *all* the weeks. The data set is 65, 65, 65, 65, 65, 78, 78, 78, 40, 40.

Summarizing Data

Data can be described by their center, spread, and distribution.

Distributions, Center, and Variability

Data can be displayed in a variety of ways that can help you study the shape, center, and spread of the values. Two such displays are a stem-and-leaf plot and a line plot.

EXAMPLE 1

The stem-and-leaf plot shows the number of points scored by a children's basketball team in each of their games. Describe the range of the data, the more common values, and the shape of the data.

```
1 | 9
2 | 7 8 8 9
3 | 0 0 1 2 3 5 5 6 8
4 | 0 1 7
5 | 8
```
Key: 3|2 means 32

▶ **Remember** An object is symmetrical if one half is a mirror image of the other half.

SOLUTION

The values range from 19 to 58. Most of the values fall in the 30s, meaning the team typically scored 30 to 39 points per game. The data are somewhat symmetrical.

To find the interquartile range, list the values from least to greatest.

19, 27, 28, 28, 29, 30, 30, 31, 32, 33, 35, 35, 36, 38, 40, 41, 47, 58

Divide the data into two equal halves. Each half should have the same number of values. This data set has 18 values in all, so place 9 values in each half.

19, 27, 28, 28, 29, 30, 30, 31, 32 | 33, 35, 35, 36, 38, 40, 41, 47, 58 ▪

EXAMPLE 2

Rick recorded the daily high temperatures in degrees Fahrenheit for his town. He summarized his data in a stem-and-leaf plot.

```
6 | 4  8
7 | 2  3  3
8 | 0  0  2  3  5  6  7
9 | 0  1  1  2  2  2  3  4
```
Key: 6|7 means 67

How many days did Rick collect data? What unit of measurement did Rick use? What are the mean and median of the data? What is the range? Describe the shape of the distribution.

▶ **Think About It** To find the number of data values in a stem-and-leaf plot, count the leaves.

SOLUTION

There are 20 values in the stem-and-leaf-plot, so Rick collected data for 20 days. The unit of measurement for the daily high temperature was degrees Fahrenheit.

mean:

$$\frac{64 + 68 + 72 + 2(73) + 2(80) + 82 + 83 + 85 + 86 + 87 + 90 + 2(91) + 3(92) + 93 + 94}{20}$$

$$= \frac{1668}{20} = 83.4$$

median: There are 20 temperatures. The median is the average of the tenth and eleventh temperatures.

$$\frac{85 + 86}{2} = 85.5$$

So half of the days had a high temperature below $85.5°$F, and half of the days had a high temperature above $85.5°$F.

range: $94 - 64 = 30$

The distribution of the data is not symmetrical. More data values fall in the 80 to 94 temperature range than in the 60s or 70s. ∎

EXAMPLE 3

In the month of April, Myra asked her friends the number of minutes they play video games on a weekday compared to the number of minutes they play on a weekend day. She displayed her data in line plots.

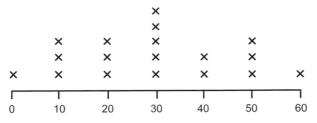

Number of Minutes Playing Video Games on a Weekday

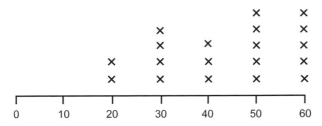

Number of Minutes Playing Video Games on a Weekend Day

Describe the best measure of center to use to describe the data sets. Describe the spread of each data set. Explain possible reasons for the differences in the two distributions.

> **Think About It** How do measures of center compare when the distribution is symmetrical?

SOLUTION

The data for time spent playing video games on a weekday are symmetrical. Because of this, the mean and median will be very close in value, if not equal. On the other hand, the data for time spent playing video games on a weekend day are not symmetrical. The data are more clustered to the middle and right. The mean and median may not be as close in value for this data set.

The spread for the two data sets also varies. The range for the first set, 60, is greater than the range for the second data set, 40.

Possible reasons that could explain the differences in the data sets are that in April, Myra's friends are likely busy with school during weekdays and have less time to play video games, whereas on the weekend they may have more time to play. ■

Outliers

An outlier is a value far away from most of the other values in a data set. But how far away is far enough?

Finding the Interquartile Range

Unless you know the spread of the data, determining whether you have an **outlier** can be hard to figure out. A data set that is widely spread is not as likely to have outliers as a data set that is less spread.

Range is one measure of spread. Another measure of spread is the **interquartile range (IQR)**. The IQR is the range of the middle half of the data set.

Formula
The IQR is the difference between the third and first quartiles.
$$IQR = Q_3 - Q_1$$

▶ **Think About It** In a box plot, the IQR is the length of the box.

The G-20 is made up of 19 countries and the European Union. Seventeen of the 19 countries have codified constitutions, or single documents stating the supreme law of the land. The chart shows the year that each of these constitutions went into effect. Find the IQR of the years.

Country	Year	Country	Year
Argentina	1853	Italy	1947
Australia	1900	Japan	1947
Brazil	1988	South Korea	1948
Canada	1867	Mexico	1917
China	1982	Russia	1993
France	1958	South Africa	1997
Germany	1949	Turkey	1982
India	1950	United States	1788
Indonesia	1945		

Order the data and find the quartiles. There are 17 data values, so the median is the ninth value, 1948. There are 8 values in the upper and lower halves.

median

1788 1853 1867 1900 | 1917 1945 1947 1947 (1948) 1949 1950 1958 1982 | 1982 1988 1993 1997

Q_1 Q_3

The first quartile is the average of the fourth and fifth values. The third quartile is the average of the 13th and 14th values.

$$Q_1 = \frac{1900 + 1917}{2} = 1908.5 \qquad Q_3 = \frac{1982 + 1982}{2} = 1982$$

Subtract. The IQR of the years is 1982 – 1908.5, or 73.5 years.

Determining Outliers

An outlier is an extremely low or high value. To help people agree on what makes a value extreme, a value is commonly considered an outlier if its distance from either Q_1 or Q_3 is more than one and a half times the IQR.

The borders between outliers and values that are not outliers are called **fences**.

Fences and Outliers

In a data set, any number less than the lower fence or greater than the upper fence is an outlier. The lower and upper fences for a data set are as follows:

$$\text{lower fence} = Q_1 - 1.5(\text{IQR})$$
$$\text{upper fence} = Q_3 + 1.5(\text{IQR})$$

Determine whether there are any outliers in the years the constitutions went into effect.

Find the lower fence.

$$
\begin{aligned}
Q_1 - 1.5(\text{IQR}) &= 1908.5 - 1.5(73.5) \\
&= 1908.5 - 110.25 \\
&= 1798.25
\end{aligned}
$$

Find the upper fence.

$$
\begin{aligned}
Q_1 + 1.5(\text{IQR}) &= 1982 + 1.5(73.5) \\
&= 1982 + 110.25 \\
&= 2092.25
\end{aligned}
$$

Years before 1798 and after 2092 are outliers, so the year that the constitution of the United States went into effect, 1788, is an outlier.

Measures of Variability

Measures of variability show the spread in a set of data.

Definitions

An **absolute deviation** is the absolute value of the difference between a data value and the mean. The **mean absolute deviation**, or MAD, is the mean of all the absolute deviations.

To find the MAD of a set of data, first calculate the absolute deviation of each data value in the data set. Then add all the absolute deviations and divide by the number of data values.

▶ **Think About It** There are other measures of variability besides the mean absolute deviation, but they often involve more complex calculations than the MAD.

EXAMPLE 1

Find the mean absolute deviation of the data.

A $\{6, 8, 11, 13, 17\}$

SOLUTION
Find the mean of the data.

$$\frac{6 + 8 + 11 + 13 + 17}{5} = \frac{55}{5} = 11$$

Calculate the absolute deviation for each data value and add.

$$|6 - 11| + |8 - 11| + |11 - 11| + |13 - 11| + |17 - 11|$$
$$= |-5| + |-3| + |0| + |2| + |6|$$
$$= 5 + 3 + 0 + 2 + 6$$
$$= 16$$

Divide the sum by the number of data values.

$$\frac{16}{5} = 3.2$$

The mean absolute deviation of the data set is 3.2.

B $\{3.1, 14.6, 19.7, 31.5, 37.8, 43.2\}$

▸ **Think About It** For large data sets, you should use a calculator to find the mean absolute deviation.

SOLUTION
Find the mean of the data.

$$\frac{3.1 + 14.6 + 19.7 + 31.5 + 37.8 + 43.2}{6} = \frac{149.9}{6} = 24.9833 \ldots \approx 25$$

Calculate the absolute deviation for each data value and add.

$$|3.1 - 25| + |14.6 - 25| + |19.7 - 25| + |31.5 - 25| + |37.8 - 25| + |43.2 - 25|$$
$$= |-21.9| + |-10.4| + |-5.3| + |6.5| + |12.8| + |18.2|$$
$$= 21.9 + 10.4 + 5.3 + 6.5 + 12.8 + 18.2$$
$$= 75.1$$

Divide the sum by the number of data values.

$$\frac{75.1}{6} = 12.51666 \ldots \approx 12.5$$

The mean absolute deviation of the data set is about 12.5. ∎

Comparing Measures of Center and Variation

A measure of center describes a data set with one value, while a measure of variation describes how the data set varies with one value.

EXAMPLE 2

The line plot shows the number of weekly activities for each teen in a group of teens.

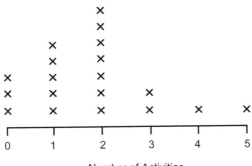

Number of Activities

A How many teens are represented in the data?

SOLUTION

There are 19 data values indicated by an x in the line plot, so there are 19 teens represented in the data.

B What are the mean and median of the data set? What do these values mean? How do they compare?

SOLUTION

mean: $\dfrac{0(3) + 1(5) + 2(7) + 3(2) + 4 + 5}{19} = \dfrac{34}{19} \approx 1.79$

median: There are 19 data values, so the median will be the middle value, or the tenth data value. The median is 2.

Because the mean is approximately 1.79, this means that if the data were equally distributed, all the teens would be involved in approximately 1.79 weekly activities. The median is 2, which means half the students are involved in 2 or more activities and half are involved in 2 or fewer activities. The median is greater than the mean, but they are very close. The mean and median are measures of center and each represent the data with a single value.

C What is the mean absolute deviation of the data? What does this value mean?

SOLUTION

Round the mean from 1.79 to 1.8 to make the calculations a little easier.

Calculate the absolute deviation for each data value.

- Find the absolute value of the difference between the mean and each data value.

- Multiply each difference by the frequency of that value.

- Find the sum of the products.

$$3 \cdot |0 - 1.8| + 5 \cdot |1 - 1.8| + 7 \cdot |2 - 1.8| + 2 \cdot |3 - 1.8| + 1 \cdot |4 - 1.8| + 1 \cdot |5 - 1.8|$$
$$= (3 \cdot 1.8) + (5 \cdot 0.8) + (7 \cdot 0.2) + (2 \cdot 1.2) + 2.2 + 3.2$$
$$= 5.4 + 4 + 1.4 + 2.4 + 2.2 + 3.2$$
$$= 18.6$$

Find the mean absolute deviation by dividing the sum by the number of data values.

$$\frac{18.6}{19} \approx 0.978947 \approx 0.98$$

The mean absolute deviation of the data set is about 0.98, or 1. This means the average distance between any data value and the mean is about 1. ■

Application: Quiz Scores

EXAMPLE 3

A teacher divided a group of 16 students into two groups of 8 students each. She recorded each student's score on a quiz.

Group 1 87, 88, 96, 91, 78, 90, 83, 95
Group 2 95, 80, 87, 76, 89, 91, 82, 96

▶ **Think About It** A data set is not always ordered from least to greatest. However, the mean absolute deviation is the same whether the data are ordered or unordered.

A Calculate the MAD of each group's quiz scores.

SOLUTION
Group 1 Calculate the mean of the quiz scores.

$$\frac{87 + 88 + 96 + 91 + 78 + 90 + 83 + 95}{8} = \frac{708}{8} = 88.5$$

Add the absolute deviations and divide the sum by the number of data items.

$$|87 - 88.5| + |88 - 88.5| + |96 - 88.5| + |91 - 88.5| + |78 - 88.5|$$
$$+ |90 - 88.5| + |83 - 88.5| + |88.5 - 95|$$
$$= |-1.5| + |-0.5| + |7.5| + |2.5| + |-10.5| + |1.5| + |-5.5| + |-6.5|$$
$$= 1.5 + 0.5 + 7.5 + 2.5 + 10.5 + 1.5 + 5.5 + 6.5 = 36$$

$$\frac{36}{8} = 4.5$$

Group 2 Calculate the mean of the quiz scores.

$$\frac{95 + 80 + 87 + 76 + 89 + 91 + 82 + 96}{8} = \frac{696}{8} = 87$$

Add the absolute deviations and divide the sum by the number of data items.

$$|95 - 87| + |80 - 87| + |87 - 87| + |76 - 87| + |87 - 89| + |87 - 91|$$
$$+ |82 - 87| + |96 - 87|$$
$$= |8| + |-7| + |0| + |-11| + |-2| + |-4| + |-5| + |9|$$
$$= 8 + 7 + 0 + 11 + 2 + 4 + 5 + 9 = 46$$

$$\frac{46}{8} = 5.75$$

The MAD of Group 1's quiz scores is 4.5. The MAD of Group 2's quiz scores is 5.75.

B Which group has the larger variation in their quiz scores? Explain your reasoning.

SOLUTION

Group 2 has the larger variation in their quiz scores. The MAD is a measure of the variation, or spread, of a set of data. Because the MAD of Group 2's scores, 5.75, is greater than the MAD of Group 1's scores, 4.5, Group 2 has the greater variation in their quiz scores. ■

Application: Manufacturing

EXAMPLE 4

A hardware manufacturer selects 9 bolts from a batch of newly made bolts. The bolt widths are 5.7, 5.8, 5.8, 5.9, 6, 6, 6, 6, and 6.1 mm.

A Find the MAD of the bolt widths. Round to the nearest hundredth.

SOLUTION

Determine the mean bolt width.

$$\frac{5.7 + 5.8 + 5.8 + 5.9 + 6 + 6 + 6 + 6 + 6.1}{9} = \frac{53.3}{9} = 5.9222 \ldots \approx 5.9$$

Calculate the MAD.

$$|5.7 - 5.9| + |5.8 - 5.9| + |5.8 - 5.9| + |5.9 - 5.9| + |6 - 5.9|$$
$$+ |6 - 5.9| + |6 - 5.9| + |6 - 5.9| + |6.1 - 5.9|$$
$$= |-0.2| + |-0.1| + |-0.1| + |0| + |0.1| + |0.1| + |0.1| + |0.1|$$
$$+ |0.2|$$
$$= 0.2 + 0.1 + 0.1 + 0 + 0.1 + 0.1 + 0.1 + 0.1 + 0.2 = 1.0$$

$$\frac{1.0}{9} = 0.111 \ldots \approx 0.11$$

The MAD of the bolt widths is 0.11 mm.

B Explain what the value of the MAD represents.

SOLUTION

The MAD is a measure of the variation in bolt widths about their mean value of 5.9 mm. The greater the MAD, the more variation there would be in the width of the bolts manufactured. ▪

Frequency Distributions

A frequency distribution is often a useful way to organize and display a data set.

Definition
A **frequency distribution** is a table or graph that describes the number of times a value or interval of values occurs in a data set.

When the frequency distribution is shown as a table, it is called a frequency table. One type of graph that shows a distribution is called a histogram.

Making a Frequency Table and a Histogram

In a frequency table or histogram, the interval sizes should be equal, and the intervals must not overlap—that is, each data value must occur in exactly one interval. Intervals are also called classes.

▶ **Think About It** How many classes should you use for your histograms? There is no one right answer. In the first example, 10 classes worked pretty well. In general, you want to use just enough classes so you can see what is happening with the data.

EXAMPLE 1

Make a frequency table for the following set of test scores. Then use the table to make a histogram.

62, 88, 95, 97, 81, 78, 65, 91, 85, 84, 98, 89, 85,
89, 72, 77, 80, 93, 97, 70, 58, 66, 94, 82, 75

SOLUTION

Step 1 Determine the number of classes you will use. As a general rule, use 5 to 15 classes. For these test scores, use 10 classes.

Step 2 Set up classes of equal width. The lowest and highest data values are 58 and 98. Convenient limits that include 58 and 98 are 50 and 100. Find the difference.

$$100 - 50 = 50$$

Divide by the number of classes.

$$50 \div 10 = 5$$

Finally, set up the classes, beginning at 50 and ending close to 100.

$$50\text{–}54, 55\text{–}59, 60\text{–}64, \ldots, 95\text{–}99$$

(Note that the first numbers of consecutive classes differ by 5: 50, 55, 60, and so on.)

Step 3 Make the frequency table. The frequency for each class is the number of times the data values in that class occur.

Class	Frequency
50–54	0
55–59	1
60–64	1
65–69	2
70–74	2
75–79	3
80–84	4
85–89	5
90–94	3
95–99	4

Step 4 Make the histogram. Use a bar to represent the frequency of each class. The greatest frequency in the table is 5, so use a scale on the Frequency axis that goes slightly higher than 5, such as 0 to 6. There should be no spaces between bars (unless a class has a frequency of 0).

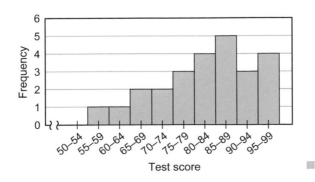

Examining Uniform, Bell-Shaped, and Skewed Distributions

The values in many data sets are distributed symmetrically. Two common symmetric distributions are the **uniform distribution** and the **bell-shaped distribution**. In a perfectly uniform distribution, all intervals have the same frequency. In a distribution that is nearly uniform or nearly bell-shaped, the mean and median are nearly equal.

▶ **Think About It** Real-world data sets are not likely to be perfectly uniform or bell-shaped. However, many real-world data sets are approximately uniform or bell-shaped.

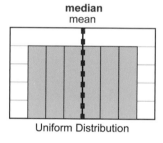

Uniform Distribution

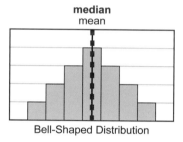

Bell-Shaped Distribution

▶ **Think About It** Skewed to the right means the mean is greater than (i.e., to the right of) the median.

Skewed to the left means the mean is less than (i.e., to the left of) the median.

In a skewed distribution, one side has lower frequencies than the other side. If the distribution is skewed to the right, the mean will be greater than the median. If the distribution is skewed to the left, the mean will be less than the median.

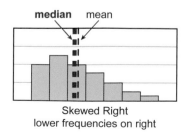

Skewed Right
lower frequencies on right

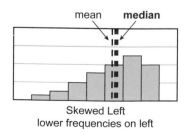

Skewed Left
lower frequencies on left

Interpreting a Frequency Table and a Histogram

EXAMPLE 2

Describe the type of distribution. Identify the relationship of the mean and the median.

A

Class	Frequency
1–15	3
16–30	2
31–45	11
46–60	17
61–75	17

SOLUTION

There are fewer data values in the classes with the lower values. This distribution is skewed left. A histogram would have lower bars on the left side than on the right side. The mean of the data set is less than the median.

B

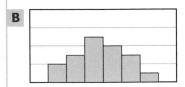

SOLUTION

The histogram is nearly bell-shaped, so the mean and median are nearly equal. ■

EXAMPLE 3

The histogram shows the distance in meters jumped by the competitors in a track meet.

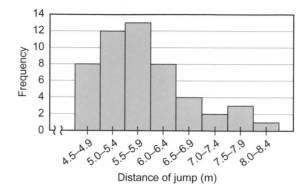

A Where are the data clumped together or spread out?

SOLUTION

Most of the data are clumped together in the classes on the left side of the distribution. So most of the competitors jumped less than a distance of 6.4 m.

B Is the distribution more closely uniform, bell, skew, or none? Why?

SOLUTION

This distribution is skewed right because there are fewer data values on the right than on the left.

C What is the relationship of the mean and the median?

SOLUTION

The average distance jumped in the track meet will be more than the median distance jumped.

D Isaiah jumped 6.4 m in the meet. About what percent of people jumped farther than Isaiah?

SOLUTION

The heights of the bars greater than 6.4 appear to be one-fourth of the height of the bars less than 6.4, so about 25% of the competitors jumped farther than Isaiah. ▪

Selecting Measures of Center

To determine the best measure of center for a data set, look at the shape of the data distribution.

Choosing an Appropriate Measure

EXAMPLE 1

The sales prices of the cars that Mario sold last month, rounded to the nearest hundreds of dollars, are shown.

11,400	31,600	23,600	22,000	11,100	23,400	69,700	17,900
12,100	17,500	15,200	17,800	81,000	28,500	10,400	

Which measure or measures of central tendency best reflect the data?

SOLUTION
Create a histogram to see the data distribution.

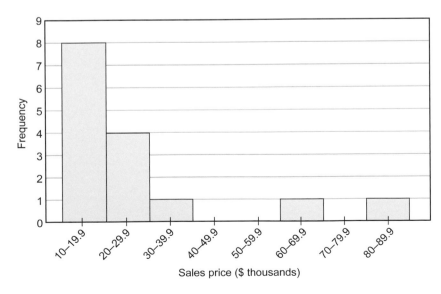

Sales price ($ thousands)

Because the data are skewed right, the mean is pulled to the right, away from the center of the distribution. The mean is not an honest reflection of the sale prices. There is no mode. The median would best reflect the data. ■

EXAMPLE 2

The numbers of traffic tickets written by each police officer in a city one day are shown.

21 11 14 16 10 18 5 16 19 20 17 5 6 10 13

Which measure or measures of central tendency best reflect the data?

SOLUTION

Create a histogram to see the data distribution.

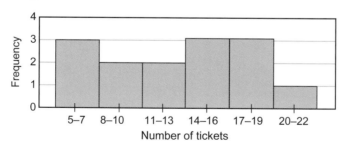

The distribution is fairly uniform, so the mean and median are approximately equal. There are three modes, 5, 10, and 16, which are not helpful since they are spread throughout the distribution. Both the mean and the median reflect the data well. ■

Pronunciation Guide

Pronunciation Guide

The tables provide sample words to explain the sounds associated with specific letters and letter combinations used in the respellings in this book. For example, *a* represents the short "a" sound in *cat*, while *ay* represents the long "a" sound in *day*.

Letter combinations are used to approximate certain more complex sounds. For example, in the respelling of *trapezoid*—TRA-puh-zoyd—the letters *uh* represent the vowel sound you hear in *shut* and *other*.

VOWELS

a	short a: **a**pple, c**a**t
ay	long a: c**a**ne, d**ay**
e, eh	short e: h**e**n, b**e**d
ee	long e: f**ee**d, t**ea**m
i, ih	short i: l**i**p, act**i**ve
iy	long i: tr**y**, m**i**ght
ah	short o: h**o**t, f**a**ther
oh	long o: h**o**me, thr**ow**
uh	short u: sh**u**t, **o**ther
yoo	long u: **u**nion, c**u**te

LETTER COMBINATIONS

ch	**ch**in, an**ci**ent
sh	**sh**ow, mi**ssi**on
zh	vi**si**on, a**z**ure
th	**th**in, heal**th**
th	**th**en, hea**th**er
ur	b**ir**d, f**ur**ther, w**or**d
us	b**us**, cr**us**t
or	c**our**t, f**or**mal
ehr	**err**or, c**ar**e
oo	c**oo**l, tr**u**e, r**u**le
ow	n**ow**, **ou**t
ou	l**oo**k, p**u**ll, w**ou**ld
oy	c**oi**n, t**oy**
aw	s**aw**, m**au**l, f**a**ll
ng	so**ng**, fi**ng**er
air	**A**ristotle, b**a**rrister
ahr	c**ar**t, m**ar**tyr

CONSONANTS

b	**b**utter, **b**aby
d	**d**og, cra**d**le
f	**f**un, **ph**one
g	**g**rade, an**g**le
h	**h**at, a**h**ead
j	**j**udge, gor**ge**
k	**k**ite, **c**ar, bla**ck**
l	**l**ily, mi**l**e
m	**m**om, ca**m**el
n	**n**ext, ca**nd**id
p	**p**rice, co**pp**er
r	**r**ubber, f**r**ee
s	**s**mall, **c**ircle, ha**ss**le
t	**t**on, po**tt**ery
v	**v**ase, **v**i**v**id
w	**w**all, a**w**ay
y	**y**ellow, ka**y**ak
z	**z**ebra, ha**z**e

Glossary

abscissa   the first number in an ordered pair of numbers; also called the *x*-coordinate

absolute deviation   the absolute value of the difference between a data value and the mean

absolute value   the distance from zero to the graph of a number on a number line; The absolute value of a number *a* is denoted by $|a|$.

acute angle   an angle that measures greater than 0° and less than 90°

acute triangle   a triangle with three acute angles

addends   numbers that are added

addition pattern   a pattern formed by adding the same addend to each term to get the next term

additive identity   a number whose sum with any given number is the given number; The additive identity for the real numbers is zero.

additive inverses   two numbers whose sum, when added together, is zero; A number's additive inverse is its opposite.

adjacent angles   angles in the same plane that share a vertex and a side but do not share any interior points

algebraic expression   an expression containing variables as well as constant values

algorithm   a step-by-step way to solve a problem

alternate exterior angles   the outside angles that do not share the same vertex and are on opposite sides of a transversal crossing two lines

alternate interior angles   the inside angles that do not share the same vertex and are on opposite sides of a transversal crossing two lines

altitude   a line segment that extends from a figure's vertex and intersects the opposite side at a right angle

angle   a figure formed by two rays, called sides, that share the same endpoint

angle of rotation   the number of degrees a figure is rotated

apothem   a line segment that joins the center of a polygon to the midpoint of one of its sides

approximate solution   an estimate for the answer to a problem

area   the number of square units contained in the interior of a figure

arrangement   the order or placement of numbers or objects

average   the sum of the data divided by the number of data values; the mean of the data

axis   a number line that appears in a graph, such as the *x*-axis or *y*-axis in a coordinate plane; The plural of *axis* is *axes*.

bar graph   a graph that uses bars to display and compare data

base   a number or variable that is raised to a given power; For example, in 5^2, 5 is the base.

base of a cylinder   one of the parallel, congruent faces of the cylinder; A base of a cylinder is a circle.

base of a figure   the bottom side or face of a geometric figure

base of a parallelogram   the side of a parallelogram that is chosen as the bottom side; Any side of a parallelogram can be its base.

base of a prism   one of two parallel congruent faces in a prism

bias   the error that can arise when a sample is not representative of its population

biased sample a sample that is not representative of its population

bisector a line that divides a line segment, an angle, or another figure into two equal parts

boundary number the upper or lower limit used to round a number to a given place value

box-and-whisker plot a diagram that shows the distribution or spread of data with the minimum, the maximum, and the three quartiles of the data

capacity a measure indicating an amount a container can hold

Cartesian coordinate system method of locating points in a plane in which the coordinates of the points are their distances from two intersecting perpendicular lines called axes

categorical variable a variable that has two or more categories

center of rotation the point about which a figure is rotated

chord a segment with endpoints that are points on a circle

circle the set of all points in a plane that are equidistant from a given point called the center

circle graph a circular chart that shows divisions according to how data results are distributed

circumference distance around a circle

clockwise in the same direction that the hands on a clock rotate

closed a set is closed under an operation if the operation performed on any two numbers in the set produces another number in the set

cluster a group of points that are close together in comparison to other points

coefficient the numerical factor in a term in a variable term

coincident system of linear equations consistent system of linear equations with infinitely many solutions; also called a consistent dependent system

collinear points points that lie on the same line

combination a collection of items in which the order of the items is not important

common factor a factor that two or more given numbers have in common; For example, 9 and 12 have a common factor of 3.

compass a tool used to draw circles and to measure in constructions

complementary angles a pair of angles for which the sum of their measures is 90°

complementary events two events such that one must occur, but both cannot occur at the same time

complex fraction a fraction that has a fraction in the numerator or the denominator (or both)

composite number a whole number greater than 1 that is not prime

compound interest interest paid on both the principal (the original amount of money) and the interest an account has already earned

cone a three-dimensional figure with one base that is a circle, a curved lateral surface, and a point called a vertex

congruent having exactly the same size and shape, even though orientation may vary

congruent angles angles that have the same measure

congruent figures figures that have the same size and shape

congruent polygons polygons that have the same size and shape

congruent triangles triangles that are identical to each other

conjecture an idea that might be true on the basis of observations but is not yet proven to be true

consecutive whole numbers whole numbers that increase by 1, such as the numbers 3, 4, and 5

consistent dependent system of linear equations a system of linear equations with infinitely many solutions; also called a coincident system

consistent independent system of linear equations   a system of linear equations with exactly one solution

consistent system of linear equations   a system having exactly one solution or infinitely many solutions

constant   a numerical term that has no variables

constant function   a function that neither rises nor falls as the input variable increases

constant of variation   the ratio of two directly proportional quantities; also the nonzero constant k defined by $y = kx$ in a direct variation; also called the constant of proportionality

constant rate   a rate that does not change over time

construction   a method showing how a figure can be drawn accurately with a specified set of tools

continuous data   values that all make sense within a range of data

contradiction   an equation that is true for no values of the variable

convenience sampling   sampling in which members of the population who are close at hand are selected

coordinate   a number that indicates the location of a point on a number line

coordinate plane   a plane that has an x-axis and a y-axis perpendicular to each other on which points can be located

corresponding angles   angles that lie in the same position or match up with respect to the transversal when the transversal crosses two lines

counterclockwise   in the opposite direction than the hands on a clock rotate

cross products   the product of the numerator of one fraction and the denominator of a second fraction and the product of the denominator of the first fraction and the numerator of the second fraction

cross section   a plane figure that results from the intersection of a plane and a solid

cube   a solid figure made up of six square faces that meet at right angles

cubed   the result of the operation where a number has been multiplied by itself two times, such as 5 cubed $= 5^3 = 5 \cdot 5 \cdot 5 = 125$; When the volume of a cube is found, the dimensions are cubed, and the volume is expressed in units cubed.

cube root   a number that when multiplied by itself 3 times equals a given number

cubic unit   a cube that is 1 unit on each side; a measure of volume

cylinder   a three-dimensional figure with two congruent, parallel bases that are circles and a curved lateral surface that joins them

data   numerical information that has been gathered; The term *data* is plural.

data skewed left   the graph of the distribution of data with a longer tail to the left side

data skewed right   the graph of the distribution of data with a longer tail to the right side

decimal   a number written with a decimal point

decreasing function   a function whose output values decrease as the input values increase

degree   a unit used to measure angles

degree of accuracy   the place value that is to be used to report an answer, such as in tens or hundredths

denominator   the bottom number of a fraction

dependent events   two events that are related in such a way that knowing about one event's occurrence has an effect on the probability of the other event

dependent variable   the output variable

diameter   a chord that passes through the center of a circle

diameter of a sphere   a line segment passing through the center of a sphere that joins two points on the sphere

difference   the solution to a subtraction problem

dilation   the change in size of a figure without a change in shape

direct linear variation   a function where y varies directly with x following the equation $y = kx$ where k is a nonzero constant

directly proportional   a relationship in which two quantities vary directly with each other

direct variation   a relationship between two quantities in which one quantity increases in proportion to the other; The relationship can be shown as a line on a graph.

discount   a decrease in the price of an item

discrete data   values that are distinct or have distinct intervals; values between the intervals that do not make sense as part of the data set

distribution of a data set   the shape of the plotted data over the range of the data set's values

distributive property   a rule that says that multiplying a number by a sum gives the same answer as multiplying the number by each addend of the sum and then adding the products

dividend   the number to be divided; The dividend divided by the divisor equals the quotient.

divide out a common factor   to simplify an expression by dividing a numerator and denominator by a common factor

divisor   the number that divides the dividend; The dividend divided by the divisor equals the quotient.

domain   the set of allowable inputs of a relation

equally likely   having the same chance of happening

equation   a number sentence that indicates that two expressions are equal

equiangular polygon   a polygon with all angles congruent

equiangular triangle   a triangle with three 60° angles

equilateral polygon   a polygon with all sides congruent

equilateral triangle   a triangle in which all three sides have equal length

equivalent   having the same value, such as $\frac{1}{2}$, 0.5, and 50%

equivalent equations   equations with the same solution or solutions

equivalent fractions   fractions with the same value

equivalent inequalities   inequalities that have the same solution set

equivalent ratios   ratios that describe the same numerical relationship

estimate (n.)   a very good guess or rough calculation of an answer, when the exact answer is not necessary

estimate (v.)   to make a very good guess or rough calculation of an answer when the exact answer is not necessary

evaluate   to find the value of an expression

evaluate a variable expression   to replace all the variables in the expression with numbers and simplify

event   a set of one or more outcomes; a subset of the sample space; also called actions

exact solution   a solution that is not an estimate or an approximation

experiment   any process or action that has a result

experimental probability   probability based on actual observations or results of an experiment

exponent   a number or variable attached to the base to show how many times the base will be a factor; For example, in 5^2, the exponent is 2.

expression   a group of mathematical symbols that represents a numerical value; Most expressions contain numerals as well as operation signs or grouping symbols or a combination of these elements. An expression containing one or more variables is a variable expression or an algebraic expression.

exterior angle of a triangle an angle formed by two sides of a triangle, one of which extends outside the triangle; Each interior angle of a triangle forms a linear pair with an exterior angle.

extrapolation the process of inferring, estimating, or predicting an unknown value that is outside of known values

extremes in a proportion, the first and last numbers or variables; In $a : b = c : d$ or $\frac{a}{b} = \frac{c}{d}$, a and d are the extremes.

factor any of two or more numbers multiplied to form a product

favorable outcome the outcome you are investigating

flip the movement of a figure that shows the figure and its mirror image, sometimes called a reflection

formula an equation that is used to compute values, such as area, perimeter, or volume

fraction a number that shows part of a set, a point on a number line, a part of a whole, a quotient, or a ratio

frequency the number of times one item appears in a data set

frequency table a table that shows how often each item appears in a set of data

friendly numbers numbers such as 5 and 10, or multiples of 5 and 10, that are easier to add, subtract, multiply, and divide

function a relation in which every element of the domain is assigned to exactly one element of the range

geometric probability the probability of an event equal to the ratio of the area of success to the area of the entire region

graph (n.) a diagram that shows the relationship between quantities

graph (v.) to draw a visual representation of data

graph of a one-variable inequality the set of points on a number line that represents all the solutions of the inequality

greatest common factor (GCF) the greatest number that divides evenly into two or more numbers

grouping symbols symbols such as parentheses, brackets, and fraction bars used to set apart an expression that should be simplified before other operations are performed

height in a geometric figure, the length of an altitude that is perpendicular to a base

height of a triangle the length of the perpendicular segment that joins a base to the opposite vertex

histogram a graph with adjoining bars; used to show the frequency of data or data groups

horizontal intercept the value of the variable on the horizontal axis at the point where a graph crosses the horizontal axis

hypotenuse the side opposite the right angle in a right triangle

identity an equation that is true for every value of the variable

image the new figure that results from a transformation

improper fraction a fraction in which the numerator is greater than or equal to the denominator

inconsistent system of linear equations a system with no solution

increasing function a function whose output values increase as input values increase

independent events two events that are related in such a way that one event's occurrence has no effect on the probability of the other event

independent variable the input variable

inequality a mathematical sentence that compares numbers or expressions using one of the symbols $<, >, \leq,$ or $\geq$

inference a conclusion reached from facts, evidence, and reasoning

input a number that will be used in a rule to determine the value of the output

integers   the set of whole numbers and their opposites $\{ \ldots -2, -1, 0, 1, 2, \ldots \}$

intercept   the value at which a graph crosses one of the coordinate axes

interest   the cost to borrow money or the amount earned by lending money

interest rate   the percentage of the original amount of money on which the interest will be calculated

interior angle   any angle inside a polygon

interpolation   the process of inferring, or estimating, an unknown value that is between known values

interquartile range (IQR)   a measure of variation found by subtracting the first quartile Q_1 from the third quartile Q_3: $IQR = Q_3 - Q_1$; represents the range of the middle half of the data

intersecting lines   lines that cross at one point

interval   the distance between two points, as between two numbers on a number line

inverse operations   opposite operations that undo each other; Subtraction and addition are inverse operations. Division and multiplication are inverse operations.

irrational number   a real number that cannot be written in the form $\frac{a}{b}$ for integers a and b, with $b \neq 0$

irregular polygon   a polygon that does not have all sides and angles equal in measure

isosceles triangle   a triangle that has at least two sides equal in length; An equilateral triangle is a special type of isosceles triangle.

label   one of the informative indicators at various places on data displays such as tables and graphs

lateral area   the sum of the areas of a figure's lateral faces only

lateral face   one of the parallelograms that form a prism and is not a base

lateral surface   the curved surface of a cylinder or cone; in a prism, any surface that connects the two bases; in a pyramid, any surface that rises from the base to the vertex

lateral surface area   the sum of the areas of all surfaces of a three-dimensional figure except the base(s)

law of large numbers   a law that states that the relative frequency of an event becomes closer to the theoretical probability of the event as the number of trials increases

least common denominator (LCD)   in a set of fractions, the least common multiple of the denominators

least common multiple (LCM)   the least number that is a multiple of all numbers in a set

leg of a right triangle   one of the two sides of a right triangle that form the right angle

like denominators   denominators that are exactly the same in two or more fractions

like fractions   fractions with the same denominator

like terms   terms that have the same variable part(s) raised to the same powers; Constants (numbers without variables) are also like terms.

line   a straight path of points that extends without end in both directions

linear association   in a scatter plot, points following a pattern that resembles a line

linear equation   an equation whose graph is a line

linear function   a function whose graph is a straight line

linear pair   two angles that have a common side and whose other sides point in opposite directions

line graph   a display in which a set of information is shown as a series of points connected by straight line segments; A line graph is used to reveal trends.

line of reflection   the line across which a figure is reflected

line plot   a number line that shows all the data values with a mark or marks above each data value to show how many times that data value occurred

line segment   part of a line including two points on the line and all the points between those points

literal equation an equation with two or more variables; Formulas are common examples of literal equations.

lower bound estimate an estimate for a problem that is less than the actual solution could be

lowest terms when the numerator and the denominator of a fraction have no common factors other than 1

magic square a square made up of an equal number of rows and columns of numbers such that the sum of any column, row, or diagonal is the same

maximum the greatest value for a data set

mean absolute deviation (MAD) the mean of all the absolute deviations of a data set

means in a proportion, the second and third numbers or variables; In $a : b = c : d$ or $\frac{a}{b} = \frac{c}{d}$, b and c are the means.

mean the sum of the values in a data set divided by the number of values

measure of center a measure that represents the center of the distribution of values for a data set, such as mean, median, and mode

measure of spread a measure that represents the extent to which the values of a data set are spread out, such as the range

measure of variation a measure, such as the interquartile range, that compares the range or spread of data to a measure of center

median the middle value when the data are ordered; If there is an even number of data values, the median is the average of the two middle values.

minimum the least value for a data set

minuend a number from which another number is subtracted

mixed number a number consisting of both a whole number and a fraction, or the opposite of such a number

mode the most common value; A data set can have no mode, one mode, or more than one mode.

multiple of a number the product of the given number and a counting number

multiplication pattern a pattern formed by multiplying each term by the same factor to get the next term

multiplicative identity the number 1

multiplicative inverse the reciprocal of a number

mutually exclusive events events that cannot happen at the same time

negative association in a scatter plot, a relationship between two variables for which an increase in one variable corresponds to a decrease in the other variable

negative correlation a trend that develops with two variables when the value of one variable increases while the other value decreases; In a scatter plot, the data points form a pattern that slants down.

negative sign the sign ($-$) indicating that a number's value is less than zero, such as -6

net a two-dimensional pattern that can be folded into a three-dimensional figure

net gain or net loss the sum of the individual values when a situation includes several gains and losses

no association in a scatter plot, a relationship between two variables for which an increase in one variable doesn't correspond to any particular pattern for the other variable

nonlinear association in a scatter plot, points following a pattern that does not resemble a line

nonlinear function a function whose graph is not a straight line

nonrepeating decimal a nonterminating decimal that has no repeating pattern of digits

nonterminating decimal a decimal that does not terminate or end

nonzero opposites two numbers that are the same distance from zero on a number line

nth root any number x such that x raised to the n power equals some given number a for a whole number $n > 1$

number line a line that has equally spaced intervals labeled with coordinates

numerator the top number of a fraction

numerical expression an expression consisting of numbers and one or more operations

obtuse angle an angle that measures greater than $90°$ and less than $180°$

obtuse triangle a triangle with an obtuse angle

open sentence an equation or inequality that contains one or more variables

opposites a pair of numbers whose distance on both sides of zero is the same, such as -5 and $+5$

ordered pair a pair of numbers in which the first number is the x-coordinate, or abscissa, and the second number is the y-coordinate, or ordinate, of a point's location in the coordinate plane

order-of-magnitude estimate an estimate expressed as a power of 10

order of operations mathematical order that should be followed to simplify an expression when there is more than one operation

ordinate the second number in an ordered pair of numbers; the y-coordinate

origin on a number line, the point with coordinate zero; on a coordinate plane, the point where the x-axis and the y-axis intersect; The ordered pair at the origin is $(0, 0)$.

outcome a result of an experiment

outlier a point that is far from other points in a data set

output the result of applying a function rule to the value of an input

parallel lines lines on the same plane that never intersect

parallelogram a quadrilateral with two pairs of parallel sides

percent a ratio that compares a number to 100

percent error the ratio of the absolute error of a measurement to the actual value, written as a percent

percent of change the ratio of the amount of change to the original amount, expressed in percent form

perfect square a rational number with a rational square root

perimeter distance around a figure; The perimeter of a polygon is the sum of the lengths of all the sides.

perpendicular lines lines that intersect and form angles that measure $90°$

place value the value of a digit depending on its position, or place, in a number

plane a flat surface with infinite length and width but no thickness

point a location in space with no length, width, or depth

point on a coordinate plane a dot that marks a coordinate; a location on a coordinate plane, designated by an x-value and a y-value

point-slope form of a linear equation $y - y_1 = m(x - x_1)$ where m is the slope of the line and x_1 and y_1 are the coordinates of a point through which the line passes

polygon a closed figure formed by three or more line segments in a plane, such that each line segment intersects two other line segments at their endpoints only

population a group of individuals or objects about which information is wanted

positive association in a scatter plot, a relationship between two variables for which an increase in one variable corresponds to an increase in the other variable

positive correlation a trend that describes when two variables increase or decrease together; In a scatter plot, the data points form a pattern that slants up.

positive sign the sign $(+)$ indicating that a number's value is greater than zero, such as $+6$; The positive sign is not always shown.

power the product that results when a number, called the base, is multiplied by itself the number of times indicated by its exponent

power of ten any number that can be written in the form $10n$, where n is an integer

precision an indication of how exact a calculation or measurement is

predict to state how future events will happen

pre-image the original figure in a transformation

prime factorization an expression showing a positive integer as a product of its prime factors

prime number a whole number greater than 1 that has only two whole-number factors, 1 and itself

principal money that earns interest at a given rate over time; The principal is the original amount of money on which the interest is based.

principal square root the nonnegative square root, indicated by the square root sign

prism a three-dimensional figure whose surfaces, called faces, are polygons; At least two faces are parallel and congruent and are called bases, and all other faces are parallelograms. (In a right prism, all other faces are rectangles.)

probability a number from 0 to 1 that describes how likely an event is to occur

product the result of multiplying two or more factors together

proper fraction a fraction in which the numerator is less than the denominator

proportion an equation stating that two ratios are equal

proportional relationship a relationship that can be described by an equation of the form $y = kx$ where k is the constant of proportionality

protractor a tool to measure the degrees in an angle

pyramid a three-dimensional figure with one base that is a polygon and all other faces (called lateral faces) are triangles that meet at a single vertex

quadrant one of the four regions into which the coordinate axes separate the coordinate plane

quadratic variation a relationship between x and y in which you can write the function describing the relationship in a form of the general equation, $f(x) = kx^2$ where k is a nonzero constant

quadrilateral a polygon with four sides

quartile one of the three values that separate an ordered data set into four equal parts; The second quartile Q_2 is the median of the data set. The first quartile Q_1 is the median of the lower half of the data set. The third quartile Q_3 is the median of the upper half of the data set. Note: A quartile also refers to the entire set of data in any quarter of the data.

quotient the result of division

radius (of a circle) a segment whose endpoints are the center of the circle and a point on the circle. The plural of *radius* is *radii*.

radius (of a sphere) a line segment joining the center of the sphere and a point on the surface of the sphere. The plural of *radius* is *radii*.

range the set of allowable outputs of a relation

range of a data set the difference of the maximum and minimum values in the data set

rate a ratio of two quantities measured in different units

rate of change the ratio of a change in one quantity to a change in a second quantity

ratio a comparison of two quantities by division

rational expression a fraction that includes expressions for the numerator or the denominator

rational number a number that can be expressed as a ratio $\frac{a}{b}$ where a and b are integers and $b \neq 0$; A rational number can be written as a fraction, a decimal, or a percent.

rational square root a square root that is a rational number

ray part of a line that begins from an endpoint and extends infinitely in one direction

reasonableness   the sense that an answer is correct, given the facts

reasoning   the series of thoughts and steps used to understand a problem, to create a plan to solve the problem, to reach a solution, and to accurately explain results

reciprocal   a number by which a given number must be multiplied to get a result of 1; also called the multiplicative inverse

rectangle   a parallelogram with four right angles; A square is a special type of rectangle.

reflection   a transformation of a figure by flipping it across a line or line segment, creating a mirror image of the figure

regular polygon   a polygon with all its sides congruent and all it angles congruent

relation   a mapping from a set of inputs to a set of outputs

relatively prime numbers   two or more numbers that have no common factors other than 1

remainder   the amount left over after dividing

repeating decimal   a decimal in which a digit, or a group of digits, other than zero repeats forever after the decimal point

replacement set   the given set of numbers that a variable may represent

representation   a way of displaying information, such as a model, a number, a graph, or an equation

rhombus   a parallelogram with four congruent sides; A square is a special type of rhombus.

right angle   an angle that measures 90°

right triangle   a triangle with a right angle

rigid transformations   transformations that do not change the size or shape of a figure

rise   the vertical change between two selected points on a line

rotation   the turning of a figure around a given point

round (v.)   to change a number to the nearest place value asked in a problem; For example, the result of rounding 532 to the nearest ten would be 530.

ruler   a tool to measure length, typically marked in centimeters or inches

run   the horizontal change between two selected points on a line

sale price   the price of an item after a discount

sales tax   a percent of the price of an item paid to a government when the item is sold

sample   part of a population

sample space   the set of all possible outcomes of an experiment

scale factor   the ratio of two corresponding sides in two similar figures

scalene triangle   a triangle that has no sides equal in length

scatter plot   a graph that displays data as points

scientific notation   a system of writing numbers as the product of a number that is greater than or equal to 1 but less than 10 and an integer power of 10

semicircle   half of a circle

sides of a polygon   the segments forming a polygon

similar figures   two figures in which each pair of corresponding angles is congruent and the ratio of the lengths of corresponding sides is constant

simple interest   interest earned at a fixed percent of the initial deposit, or principal amount

simple random sampling   sampling in which all members of the population have an equal probability of selection

simplest form of a fraction   a fraction in which the numerator and the denominator have no common factor other than 1 or -1

simplify a numerical expression   to find the value of a numerical expression

slide   the movement of a figure along a line without turns or flips, also known as translation

slope-intercept form of a linear equation
$y = mx + b$ where m is the slope of the line and b is the y-intercept

slope of a line   the ratio of the vertical change, or rise, between any two points on the line to the horizontal change, or run, between the same two points

solution   the answer to a problem or the process used to find the answer

solution of an open sentence   a number that makes the open sentence true

solution set   the set of all solutions to a given open sentence

solve   to find the value(s) of the variable(s) that make an equation true

speed   the ratio of distance traveled to time

sphere   the set of all points in space that are a given distance from a point called the center

square   a parallelogram with four congruent sides and four right angles

squared   the result of the operation where a number has been multiplied by itself, such $5^2 = 5 \cdot 5 = 25$; When the area of a square is found, the dimensions are squared, and the area is expressed in units squared.

square of a number   the product of a number and itself

square root   a factor of a number that when multiplied by itself results in the number; The nonnegative square root is called the principal square root and is indicated by the square root sign.

square unit   a square with sides of a particular side length, such as a square meter, used to measure area

standard form of a linear equation $Ax + By = C$ where A, B, and C are integers, and A and B are both nonzero

standard form of a number   a number expressed using digits and place values

stem-and-leaf plot   data display that lists the last digits (leaves) of the data values to the right of the earlier digits (stems)

straight angle   an angle that measures 180°

strategy   a technique used to solve a problem, such as working backward or drawing a diagram

stratified random sampling   sampling in which the population is first organized into separate categories, and then each is sampled as an independent subpopulation

substitution   the replacement of an equivalent value for another

subtrahend   a number that is subtracted from another number

sum   the result of an addition; The numbers added are addends.

supplement   one of two supplementary angles

supplementary angles   a pair of angles for which the sum of their measures is 180°

surface area   the sum of the areas of all surfaces of a three-dimensional figure

surface area of a rectangular prism   the sum of the areas of a prism's lateral faces and two bases

surface of a solid figure   all of the polygons that are faces of the solid figure

survey   a strategy for collecting data by asking questions of a group of people

systematic sampling   sampling in which the population is ordered, and then members are selected at regular intervals through that ordered list

system of linear equations   two or more linear equations using the same variables

tax   a sum of money collected by a government

term   a part of an expression that can be a number, a variable, or a product of numbers and variables

term in a pattern   each number or object in a pattern

terminating decimal   a decimal that has a finite number of nonzero digits to the right of the decimal point

term number   the position of a term in a pattern

tessellation a pattern of shapes that fit together with no overlaps or gaps and can extend to fill a figure

theoretical probability the ratio of the number of favorable outcomes to the total number of possible outcomes

three-dimensional object a figure with length, width, and height; often called 3-D

tip an amount of money given to someone who provides a service

transformation (geometric) a movement or change of a figure, such as a translation, reflection, rotation, or dilation

transformation (of an equation) any change to an equation that results in an equivalent equation

translation a sliding of a figure in a straight path without rotation or reflection

transversal a line that intersects two or more lines in a plane

trapezoid a quadrilateral with exactly one pair of parallel sides

tree diagram a branching diagram used in probability to show outcomes of several events that occur one after the other

trend a consistent pattern in data

triangle a figure made up of three segments joined at their endpoints; Each endpoint is a vertex.

turn the movement of a figure a certain number of degrees around a given point, sometimes called a rotation

two-dimensional shape a figure with length and width, but no height; often called 2-D

two-way relative frequency table a table that shows the relative frequencies of each data value in a two-way table

two-way table a frequency table for two categorical variables

unbiased sample a sample that is representative of the population

unit an object or an amount used to measure, such as kilograms as a standard unit for mass

unit rate a rate in which the second quantity in the ratio is 1

unlike denominators denominators that are different in two or more fractions

upper bound estimate an estimate for a problem that is greater than the actual solution could be

variable a symbol that represents a value

variable expression an expression consisting of one or more variables, one or more operations, and possibly one or more numbers; also called an algebraic expression

vector a line segment with a direction indicated with an arrow

Venn diagram a drawing that shows relationships among sets of numbers or objects

vertex a point where two sides of a polygon meet. The plural of *vertex* is *vertices*.

vertical angles two nonadjacent angles that share a vertex and are formed by two intersecting lines

vertical intercept the value of the variable on the vertical axis at the point where a graph crosses the vertical axis

volume a measure of space inside a figure

whole number any member of the set $\{0, 1, 2, 3, 4, \ldots\}$

x-axis in a coordinate plane, the horizontal line, or axis

x-coordinate the first number in an ordered pair of numbers; also called the abscissa

x-intercept the x-coordinate of a point where a graph intersects the x-axis

y-axis in a coordinate plane, the vertical line, or axis

y-coordinate the second number in an ordered pair of numbers; also called the ordinate

y-intercept of a graph the y-coordinate of the point where the graph intersects the y-axis; also called the vertical intercept

Symbols

|	such that		$-a$	the opposite of a
$\in$	is an element of		a^n	a to the nth power
$\varnothing$ or {}	null or empty set		$\{\ldots\}$	description or list of all elements in a set; roster notation
$\sqrt{a}$	principal square root of a			
$\sqrt[3]{a}$	cube root of a		%	percent
A'	A prime; the result of transforming point A		—	placed over a digit or a block of digits in a decimal to show that the digit or block of digits repeats
$\ldots$	continuation of a pattern			
Q_1	first quartile		$\pm$	plus or minus
x_1	first value of x		$a:b$	ratio of a to b
π	pi		$^\circ$	degree
( )	parentheses		$\overline{AB}$	line segment AB
[ ]	brackets		AB	length of line segment AB
$\approx$	is approximately equal to		$\overrightarrow{AB}$	ray AB
$=$	is equal to		$\overleftrightarrow{AB}$	line AB
$\neq$	is not equal to		$\triangle ABC$	triangle ABC
$\cong$	is congruent to		$\angle ABC$	angle ABC
$\sim$	is similar to		$m\angle ABC$	the measure of angle ABC
$<$	is less than		⌐	right angle
$>$	is greater than		$\parallel$	is parallel to
$\leq$	is less than or equal to		$\perp$	is perpendicular to
$\geq$	is greater than or equal to			
$|x|$	absolute value of x			

Properties

Real Number Properties

Let a, b, and c be any real numbers.

Addition Property of Equality	If $a - b$, then $a + c = b + c$ and $c + a = c + b$.
Addition Property: Addends with Like Signs	For all $a > 0$ and $b > 0$, $a + b = |a| + |b|$. For all $a < 0$ and $b < 0$, $a + b = -|a| + |b|$.
Addition Property: Addends with Unlike Signs	For all $a > 0$ and $b < 0$, $\quad$ If $|a| > |b|$, then $a + b = |a| - |b|$. $\quad$ If $|a| < |b|$, then $a + b = -|b| - |a|$.
Subtraction Property of Equality	If $a = b$, then $a - c = b - c$.
Substitution Property of Equality	If $a = b$, then a may be replaced with b in any expression or equation.
Multiplication Property of Equality	If $a = b$, then $c \cdot a = c \cdot b$ and $a \cdot c = b \cdot c$.
Division Property of Equality	If $a = b$ and $c \neq 0$, then $\dfrac{a}{c} = \dfrac{b}{c}$.
Distributive Property	$a(b + c) = ab + ac$

	Addition	Multiplication
Commutative Properties	$a + b = b + a$	$a \cdot b = b \cdot a$
Associative Properties	$(a + b) + c = a + (b + c)$	$(a \cdot b) \cdot c = a \cdot (b \cdot c)$
Inverse Properties	$a + (-a) = 0$ and $(-a) + a = 0$	$a \cdot \dfrac{1}{a} = 1$ and $\dfrac{1}{a} \cdot a = 1$, $a \neq 0$
Identity Properties	$a + 0 = a$ and $0 + a = a$	$a \cdot 1 = a$ and $1 \cdot a = a$

Absolute Value Equations

If $|x| = a$ for some positive number a, then $x = a$ or $x = -a$.

Properties of Exponents

Let a and b be nonzero real numbers. Let m and n be integers.

If n is a positive integer, then $a^n = a \cdot a \cdot a \cdot \ldots \cdot a$ (n factors).

Zero Exponent Property	$a^0 = 1, a \neq 0$
Negative Exponent Property	$a^{-m} = \dfrac{1}{a^m}, a \neq 0$
Product of Powers Property	$a^m \cdot a^n = a^{m+n}$

Square Root Properties

For nonnegative values of m, n, and p, if $m < n < p$, then $\sqrt{m} < \sqrt{n} < \sqrt{p}$.

Product Property	For real numbers a and b, $\sqrt{ab} = \sqrt{a} \cdot \sqrt{b}$ and $\sqrt{a} \cdot \sqrt{b} = \sqrt{ab}$.
Quotient Property	For real numbers a and b with $b \neq 0$, $\sqrt{\dfrac{a}{b}} = \dfrac{\sqrt{a}}{\sqrt{b}}$.

Reciprocal Properties

Reciprocal Property of Multiplication	For any nonzero real number a, $a \cdot \dfrac{1}{a} = 1$.

For all nonzero real numbers a and b, the reciprocal of $\dfrac{a}{b}$ is $\dfrac{b}{a}$.

For any nonzero real number a, $\dfrac{1}{-a} = \dfrac{-1}{a} = -\dfrac{1}{a}$.

For all nonzero real numbers a and b, $\dfrac{1}{ab} = \dfrac{1}{a} \cdot \dfrac{1}{b}$.

Division Properties

For any real number a and nonzero real number b, $a \div b = a \cdot \dfrac{1}{b}$.

For all real numbers a and b and nonzero real number c, $a + \dfrac{b}{c} = \dfrac{a}{c} + \dfrac{b}{c}$.

For all $a > 0$ and $b > 0$, $a \div b > 0$.

For all $a < 0$ and $b < 0$, $a \div b > 0$.

For all $a < 0$ and $b > 0$, $a \div b < 0$.

Properties of Order

Comparison Property of Order	If $a > b$, then $b < a$. If $a < b$, then $b > a$.
Transitive Property of Order	If $a > b$ and $b > c$, then $a > c$. If $a < b$ and $b < c$, then $a < c$.
Addition Property of Order	If $a > b$, then $a + c > b + c$. If $a < b$, then $a + c < b + c$.
Subtraction Property of Order	If $a > b$, then $a - c > b - c$. If $a < b$, then $a - c < b - c$.
Multiplication Property of Order, Positive Multiplier	If $a > b$ and $c > 0$, then $ca > cb$ and $ac > bc$. If $a < b$ and $c > 0$, then $ca < cb$ and $ac < bc$.
Multiplication Property of Order, Negative Multiplier	If $a > b$ and $c < 0$, then $ca < cb$ and $ac < bc$. If $a < b$ and $c < 0$, then $ca > cb$ and $ac > bc$.
Division Property of Order, Positive Multiplier	If $a > b$ and $c > 0$, then $\dfrac{a}{c} > \dfrac{b}{c}$. If $a < b$ and $c > 0$, then $\dfrac{a}{c} < \dfrac{b}{c}$.
Division Property of Order, Negative Multiplier	If $a > b$ and $c < 0$, then $\dfrac{a}{c} < \dfrac{b}{c}$. If $a < b$ and $c < 0$, then $\dfrac{a}{c} > \dfrac{b}{c}$.

Comparison Property of Rational Numbers

For nonzero integers a and c and positive integers b and d,

$\dfrac{a}{b} > \dfrac{c}{d}$ if, and only if, $ad > bc$.

$\dfrac{a}{b} < \dfrac{c}{d}$ if, and only if, $ad < bc$.

Properties of Proportions

Let a, b, c, and d be real numbers.

Means-Extremes Product Property	$\dfrac{a}{b} = \dfrac{c}{d}$ if, and only if, $ad = bc$, given that b and d are not 0.
Reciprocal Property	If $\dfrac{a}{b} = \dfrac{c}{d}$, then $\dfrac{b}{a} = \dfrac{d}{c}$, given that a, b, c, and d are all nonzero.

Formulary

Geometry

CIRCLE

circumference $\quad C = \pi d = 2\pi r$

area $\quad A = \pi r^2$

CONE

volume $\quad V = \frac{1}{3}Bh = \frac{1}{3}\pi r^2 h$

CYLINDER

volume $\quad V = Bh = \pi r^2 h$

surface area $\quad S = 2\pi r^2 + 2\pi rh$

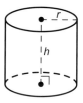

PARALLELOGRAM

area $A = bh$

PRISM: CUBE

volume $V = s^3$

surface area $S = 6s^2$

lateral area of a prism $L = Ph$

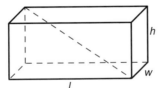

PRISM: RIGHT RECTANGULAR

volume $V = lwh$

surface area $S = 2lw + 2lh + 2wh$

length of diagonal $d = \sqrt{l^2 + w^2 + h^2}$

PYRAMID

volume $V = \frac{1}{3}Bh$

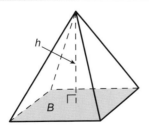

SPHERE

volume $V = \frac{4}{3}\pi r^3$

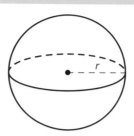

RECTANGLE

area $A = lw$

perimeter $P = 2l + 2w$

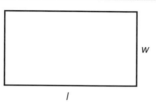

REGULAR POLYGON WITH n SIDES

perimeter of regular polygon $P = ns$

area of regular polygon $A = \frac{1}{2}aP$

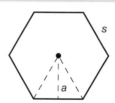

SQUARE

area $A = s^2$

perimeter $P = 4s$

TRAPEZOID

area $\quad A = \frac{1}{2}h\left(b_1 + b_2\right)$

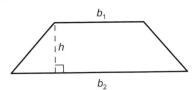

TRIANGLE: GENERAL

area $\quad A = \frac{1}{2}bh$

perimeter $\quad P = a + b + c$

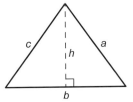

TRIANGLE: RIGHT

Pythagorean theorem $\quad a^2 + b^2 = c^2$

Coordinate Geometry

LINE

slope $\quad m = \dfrac{\text{rise}}{\text{run}} = \dfrac{\text{vertical change}}{\text{horizontal change}} = \dfrac{y_2 - y_1}{x_2 - x_1}$

linear equation: standard form
$Ax + By = C$

linear equation: slope-intercept form
$y = mx + b$

linear equation: point-slope form
$y - y_1 = m\left(x - x_1\right)$

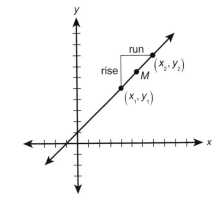

VERTICAL DISTANCE

same x-value $d = y_2 - y_1$

HORIZONTAL DISTANCE

same y-value $d = x_2 - x_1$

DIRECT LINEAR VARIATION

general formula $y = kx$ $k \neq 0$

QUADRATIC VARIATION

general formula $y = kx^2$ $k \neq 0$

Probability

SIMPLE THEORETICAL PROBABILITY

$$P(E) = \frac{\text{number of outcomes in event } E}{\text{total number of outcomes in sample space } S} = \frac{n(E)}{n(S)}$$

PROBABILITY OF MUTUALLY EXCLUSIVE EVENTS

$$P(A \text{ or } B) = P(A) + P(B)$$

RELATIVE FREQUENCY OF AN EVENT (EXPERIMENTAL PROBABILITY)

If n is the number of trials of an experiment or number of observations in a study, then the relative frequency of an event E is

$$P(E) = \frac{\text{number of times event } E \text{ has occurred}}{n}.$$

PROBABILITY OF INDEPENDENT EVENTS

For independent events A and B,
$$P(A \text{ and } B) = P(A) \bullet P(B).$$

PROBABILITY OF DEPENDENT EVENTS

For dependent events A and B,

$$P(A \text{ and } B) = P(A) \bullet P(B \text{ after } A)$$

where $P(B \text{ after } A)$ is the probability of B knowing that event A has already occurred.

GEOMETRIC PROBABILITY

$$P(E) = \frac{\text{area of region of success}}{\text{area of entire region}}$$

Statistics

MEAN

$$\bar{x} = \frac{x_1 + x_1 + \ldots + x_n}{n}$$

ABSOLUTE DEVIATION

The absolute deviation is the absolute value of the difference between a data value and the mean.

MEAN ABSOLUTE DEVIATION (MAD)

The MAD is the mean of all the absolute deviations. Calculate the absolute deviation for each data value and add. Then divide the sum by the number of data value.

MEANS-TO-MAD RATIO

$$\frac{|\bar{x}_1 + \bar{x}_2|}{\text{MAD}_{\text{larger}}}$$

MEDIAN

Arrange the values in order from least to greatest. For an

    Odd number of values, use the middle value.

    Even number of values, use the average of the middle two values.

MODE

The mode is the value that occurs most often in a set of data. If no one value occurs most often, then there is no mode for the set.

RANGE

$$\text{range} = \text{maximum} - \text{minimum}$$

Conversions

CONVERSION FOR LENGTH

English Units

1 ft = 12 in.

1 yd = 36 in.

1 yd = 3 ft

1 mi = 5280 ft

Metric Units

1 cm = 10 mm

1 m = 100 cm

1 km = 1000 m

CONVERSION OF CUBIC UNITS

English Units

$1 \text{ ft}^3 = 1728 \text{ in}^3$

$1 \text{ yd}^3 = 27 \text{ ft}^3$

Metric Units

$1 \text{ cm}^3 = 1000 \text{ mm}^3$

$1 \text{ m}^3 = 1,000,000 \text{ cm}^3$

SCALE FACTOR FORMULAS

If SA_F is the surface area of a figure that is enlarged or reduced with a scale factor, then the surface area of the scaled image, SA_I, is $SA_I = (\text{scale factor})^2 \cdot SA_F$.

General Applications

$$\text{percent of change} = \frac{\text{amount of change}}{\text{original amount}} \cdot 100\%$$

$$I = Prt$$

where I is the amount of interest, P is the principal (the money you start with or your first deposit), r is the annual interest rate, and t is the time in years.

$$A = P\left(1 + r\right)^t$$

where P is the principal (the money you start with or your first deposit), r is the interest rate, and t is the number of years.

$$\text{percent error} = \frac{\left|\text{measured value} - \text{actual value}\right|}{\text{actual value}} \cdot 100\%$$

$$\text{percent of total cost} = \frac{\text{individual cost}}{\text{total cost}} \cdot 100\%$$

$$\text{final price} = \text{pre-tax price} + \text{tax paid}$$

Illustrations Credits

All illustrations © K12 Inc. unless otherwise noted

Front cover Peacock. © Dobrynina Elena/Shutterstock

Back cover Splash watercolor. © Dobrynina Elena/Shutterstock

K¹² Summit Curriculum Computer monitor. © antpkr/Shutterstock; Tablet and phone. © Radu Bercan/Shutterstock

Number Properties Enigma machine. © John Robertson/Alamy Stock Photo

Fractions and Decimals Violins. © Cusp/Superstock

Rational Numbers Stock ticker. © msenbg/Fotolia

Expressions Fence in a field. © David Stubbs/Aurora Photos

Equations and Inequalities Ice climber. © Minden Pictures/Getty Images

Ratios, Rates, and Percents Mosquito. © Love Silhouette/Shutterstock

Area, Surface Area, and Volume Students studying. © James Lauritz/moodboard/Corbis

Statistical Graphs Bike race. © Mike Powell/Getty Images

Measures of Center and Spread Sea urchin shells. © Ingrid Maasik/Shutterstock

Data Sources

STATISTICAL GRAPHS

NCAA. 2016. "Women's Soccer Championship History." Accessed May 3, 2016.
http://www.ncaa.com/history/soccer-women/d1.